NASW
National Association of Social Work

MW00611345

HEALTH & SOCIAL WORK

A JOURNAL OF THE NATIONAL ASSOCIATION OF SOCIAL WORKERS

http://www.naswpress.org

TABLE OF CONTENTS

Put it in writing!
Call for Book Proposals

NASW Press publishes high-quality professional books of relevance to social workers and other professionals in social welfare and the human services.

We welcome proposals on a variety of topics and seek submissions for scholarly works, textbooks, reference works, practice books, and guidebooks.

In general, NASW Press focuses on publishing books that contribute to the advancement of knowledge and practice in social work.

NASW PRESS

PROPOSAL REQUIREMENTS

Prospective authors should submit a completed NASW Press Book Proposal Packet, which they may obtain by contacting Acquisitions Editor Rachel Meyers or downloading it from the Author Center section of the NASW Press Web site (www.naswpress.org/content/1423). This brief packet contains two sections: one with questions about the book's author(s), content, and target market, and one that explains the required attachments (curriculum vitae, annotated table of contents, and sample chapter).

One electronic copy (in Microsoft Word) should be sent to Acquisitions Editor Rachel Meyers (rmeyers.nasw@socialworkers.org). Please type "Book Proposal Packet" in the subject line. For more detailed information, visit Write for Us at www.naswpress.org.

Health & Social Work (ISSN 0360-7283) is a professional journal committed to improving social work practice and extending knowledge in the field of health. Health is defined broadly to include both physical and mental health. The editorial board welcomes manuscripts that deal with all aspects of health that are of professional concern to social workers—for example, practice, social policy and planning, legislative issues, innovation, and research. Statements of fact and opinion in the articles in *Health & Social Work* are those of the authors and contributors, not of NASW Press or Oxford University Press, and do not necessarily reflect the official position of NASW or Oxford University Press. Neither NASW Press nor Oxford University Press makes any representation, express or implied, regarding the accuracy of the material in this journal and cannot accept any legal responsibility or liability for any errors or omissions that may be made. The reader should make his or her own evaluation as to the appropriateness or otherwise of any experimental technique described.

In the interest of accurate and unbiased communication, NASW subscribes to a belief in the importance of avoiding language that might imply sexual, racial, ethnic, or other kinds of discrimination, stereotyping, or bias. NASW is committed to the fair and equal treatment of individuals and groups, and material submitted should not promote stereotypes or discriminatory attitudes and assumptions about people.

Advertising rates are available on request. Publication of an advertisement does not constitute an endorsement or approval of any products or services advertised, any point of view, standard, or opinion presented therein. NASW is not responsible for any claims made in an advertisement appearing in its publications. To advertise, please contact Linda Hann: linda.hann@oup.com. Tel: +44 (0)1367 710022 (please call during UK working hours only).

Published quarterly in February, May, August, and November by the National Association of Social Workers, 750 First Street, NE, Suite 800, Washington, DC 20002-4241

Print subscription rates: NASW members, $103 for 1 year; NASW student members, $67 for 1 year; nonmembers: individuals, $170 for 1 year; libraries/institutions, $274 for 1 year; corporate, $342 for 1 year. For a print subscription, please contact Oxford Journals at jnlorders@oup.com or 1(800) 852-7323. For online subscription, go to http://naswpress.org/publications/journals/hsw.html

Health & Social Work is indexed/abstracted in *Abstracts in Anthropology; Abstracts in Social Gerontology; Academic Abstracts; AgeLine; Applied Social Sciences Index & Abstracts (ASSIA); caredata, Cumulative Index to Nursing & Allied Health Literature (CINAHL); ERIC/Cass; Exceptional Children Education Resources; Medline; Psychological Abstracts/PsycINFO/PsycLIT; Public Affairs Information Services Bulletin (PAIS); Sage Family Studies Abstracts; Social Sciences Citation Index; Social Sciences Index/Social Sciences Abstracts; Social Work Abstracts; and Sociological Abstracts (SA)/Social Planning, Policy, and Development Abstracts (SOPODA)*

National Headquarters and Publishing Office: National Association of Social Workers, 750 First Street, NE, Suite 800, Washington, DC 20002-4241. Telephone: 202-408-8600, 800-638-8799, TTD 202-336-8396. http://www.naswpress.org

Periodical class mail postage paid at Washington, DC, and at additional mailing offices. Postmaster: Send address changes to Journals Customer Service Department, Oxford University Press, 4000 CentreGreen Way, Suite 310, Cary, NC 27513, USA

Managing Ethical and Ideological Practice Conflicts in a Polarizing Political Environment

Christine M. Rine

As the 2024 presidential election nears, personal and professional repercussions of its outcome are likely at the forefront of our thoughts and concerns. The potential bearing on the health and well-being of those we serve is unimaginable. The threat of profound policy upheaval stretches across an array of pivotal social, economic, and environmental justice issues, with acutely devastating implications for diversity, equity, and inclusion efforts. Our work to promote social justice may be at an all-time high leading up to this pivotal ballot. As a result, community organizing, advocacy, policy advancement, and political action endeavors are apt to be more intense and evident within our workplaces and noticeable to our clients. The current social climate serves to intensify the capacity for ethical and ideological conflicts in practice settings due to staunch polarization, partisan division, and public dissatisfaction with the state of politics as a whole. Seeking balance between social justice and client interests is challenging in the best of circumstances. However, the present sociopolitical environment is prone to exacerbating conflict. Navigating disagreement is exceptionally precarious when the political ideologies of those with whom we work might be incongruent with their goals and their own best interests. Given that social justice principles are at the core of the profession's values, it is surprising that there is little attention and guidance for social workers around managing politically driven discord.

Understanding the ethical context of balancing social justice principles with conflicting client positions is advanced in Frederick Reamer's Eye on Ethics piece, "When Politics Enters the Room" in *Social Work Today* magazine (Reamer, 2019). This column is helpful in framing the profession's unique commitment to social justice and explores the strengths and limitations of the National Association of Social Workers (NASW, 2021) *Code of Ethics* in guiding us through negotiating politically charged ethical dilemmas. Reamer presents a clear statement of the problem at hand:

> Here is the ethical conundrum: On one side of the proverbial coin, social workers are exhorted to address social justice and social change issues. The NASW *Code of Ethics* says so. NASW's CEO says so. In this respect, social justice and social change are in social workers' professional DNA. On the coin's other side, however, are the boundary issues that can and sometimes do emerge when social workers pursue their moral mission. Social workers who serve individual clients know quite well that clients' interests are primary. (Reamer, 2019, p. 30)

This article concludes by suggesting professional self-awareness to manage ethical uncertainties that arise from social justice activities and political disagreement.

For many of us in direct practice settings, what we do when this conundrum emerges is of mounting importance as sentiments intensify leading up to November 5. An article titled "Navigating Political Disagreement in Social Work: An Analysis of Past Literature, Ethical Guidance, and Case Examples" brings to light the complexity of these situations and provides direction for further consideration (Addison, 2022). This work carefully reviews previous international literature illustrating politically charged professional interactions to inform social work practice in the United States. This is particularly relevant due to rising tensions in our current sociopolitical climate that necessitates increased attention and direction that is more explicit. Strategies to manage conflict are developed through case examples and summarized in graphic depictions of how political belief disclosure has been addressed in the literature and in a client-centered decision-making model of practice recommendations for tackling political topics.

Recognizing and managing ethical and ideological conflicts in practice is a challenging but necessary task for the profession and one that social workers are well equipped to tackle. We are adept at professional self-reflection and leading difficult conversations, both of which are the initial and fundamental steps in negotiating political disagreement with clients. Striving for an ethical balance between our social justice principles and conflicting client perspectives is an ongoing process that merits further attention, responsiveness, and discourse, and it will continue to be critical postelection regardless of the outcome. **HSW**

REFERENCES

Addison, S. M. (2022). Navigating political disagreement in social work: An analysis of past literature, ethical guidance, and case examples. *Journal of Purdue Undergraduate Research*, *12*, Article 2. https://doi.org/10.7771/2158-4052.1572

National Association of Social Workers. (2021). *Code of Ethics of the National Association of Social Workers.* https://www.socialworkers.org/About/Ethics/Code-of-Ethics/Code-of-Ethics-English

Reamer, F. G. (2019). Eye on ethics: When politics enters the room. *Social Work Today, 19*, 30–31. https://www.socialworktoday.com/archive/MJ19p30.shtml

Christine M. Rine, PhD, *is professor, Department of Social Work, Sociology, and Human Services, Penn West University, 235 Scotland Road, Hendricks Hall G-37, Edinboro, PA 16444, USA; email: crine@pennwest.edu.*

Advance Access Publication March 19, 2024

COVID-19 and the Postviral Syndrome of Long COVID: Where We Have Come from and Where We Are Going

Susan A. Taylor and Nancy J. Smyth

The world was introduced to the severe acute respiratory syndrome coronavirus 2 (SARS-CoV-2, otherwise known as COVID-19) after it was detected in Wuhan, China, in December of 2019. The fast-spreading virus caused the World Health Organization (WHO) to first declare a public health emergency of international concern (PHEIC) on January 30, 2020, later followed by declaring the outbreak a pandemic on March 11, 2020 (Jee, 2020; WHO, 2023). Shortly after WHO's declarations, the Trump administration, through the Secretary of U.S. Department of Health and Human Services (HHS), issued its first public health emergency declaration regarding COVID-19 on January 31, 2020, under section 319 of the Public Health Service Act (42 U.S.C 247d; HHS, 2020) later followed with a pandemic declaration on March 13, 2020 (White House, Executive Office of the President, 2020). The PHEIC and pandemic declarations from both the WHO and Trump administration were the administrative mechanisms allowing for redirection of resources toward increased health surveillance, laboratory research toward vaccines, releasing of strategic stockpiles, issuance of travel bans and stay-at-home orders, and other mechanisms of international and national cooperation designed to contain the virus, support strained healthcare systems, and encourage a positive public response (AJMC, 2021). The definitional nuances for the PHEIC (WHO, 2023) and the pandemic (Kelly, 2011)—clarified through complex policy language and directives—initially received buy-in from an unprepared global public. However, often conflicting messaging from public health and governmental officials (Ratzan et al., 2020) led to increased confusion among the general public, and acceptance began to wane after the first year and a half of the declarations (De Wit et al., 2023; Northwestern Institute for Policy Research, 2023).

The international and national declarations of both a PHEIC and pandemic stayed in place from 2020 through 2023. On May 5, 2023, the WHO Emergency Committee on COVID-19 stated that the virus no longer fit the definition of a PHEIC and rescinded the declaration (WHO, n.d.). In the same announcement, however, WHO also stated, "This does not mean that the global pandemic itself is over, but the global emergency it caused is—for now" (WHO, n.d., para. 3). The Biden administration announced the public health emergency was officially over on May 11, 2023 (White House, 2023), and began dismantling many of the major aspects of COVID-19 support. The effects of ending the declaration were far-reaching for the general public (Cubanski et al., 2023). Likewise, President Biden's statement in an interview on CBS *60 Minutes* that the pandemic was over (CBS News, 2022) and had become "endemic" was widely reported by the print and broadcast media and condemned by some medical health experts as premature and adding confusion in the public sphere (Williams, 2022). Of note is that the terms *pandemic, epidemic,* and *endemic,* as they have been defined in public health (Columbia University Mailman School of Public Health, 2021), have nothing to do with the virology per se or a virus's severity of risk to the public; rather, these terms are related to the location and breadth of an outbreak.

The public health and governmental messaging regarding the nuances of these declarations, and the controversial decision to rescind them; how and if the public should continue to protect themselves; funding for COVID-19-related healthcare; and how communities could best mediate viral spread became increasingly more convoluted (Gulumbe & Yusuf,

2023; Kupferschmidt & Wadman, 2023; Tyson & Funk, 2022; Vales, 2023). Public health messaging became victim to politics, misrepresentation and miscommunication of health consequences on social media, and pandemic fatigue combined to exacerbate the public's willingness to continue to engage in standard public health practices (e.g., vaccines, masking, handwashing, social distancing, and improved ventilation in public as well as private spaces; Freckelton, 2020). The fast-mutating aerosolized nature of the virus, its uneven debilitating and oftentimes lethal consequences across populations, as well as its surpassing of medical research, along with the absence of eradicating treatments have left global populations vulnerable to continued harm four years into what WHO continues in 2024 to call the COVID-19 pandemic. The administrative decisions internationally and nationally to discontinue the public health declarations with respect to COVID-19, as well as the continuing mutations of the virus (European Centre for Disease Prevention and Control, 2024), have provided a tragic Faustian bargain for public health professionals, the medical establishment, and government officials, all of whom continue to witness the ravages of COVID-19 on individuals, families, communities, economies, as well as the social fabric of nations (Bonotti & Zech, 2021; McNeely & Schintler, 2020).

With every new variant of COVID-19 comes a rise in Long COVID cases, a postviral syndrome that has prolonged the personal and financial misery of a significant number of individuals infected with various strains of the virus (Agergaard et al., 2023; Du et al., 2022). The now well-documented but elusive emerging public health crisis of post-COVID disability (Burns, 2022; National Academies of Sciences, Engineering, and Medicine, 2022) was recognized early in the pandemic with the Biden administration officially categorizing it as a disability eligible for accommodations (Social Security Administration, 2023; Stephenson, 2022). At this stage in crisis, the new variants and continuing disabling condition of the post-viral syndrome of Long COVID have prolonged a pandemic that is assumed by the public to be over (Otto et al., 2021). With the addition of Long COVID to the public health risk, there is potential for social, economic, and political instability nationally and globally for many years into the future (International Monetary Fund, 2020).

LONG COVID

Although COVID-19 was first thought to be only an acute respiratory illness, it is now clear that the virus can manifest in multiple systems of the body, including cardiovascular, neurological, immune, gastrointestinal, reproductive, musculoskeletal, and respiratory, long after the acute phase of the illness is over (Davis et al., 2023; Li et al., 2023). These systemic manifestations are referred to as Long COVID or post-COVID-19 conditions, terms coined by people with this condition (HHS, n.d.). The medical term for Long COVID is post-acute sequelae of SARS-CoV-2 infection (HHS, n.d.).

Long COVID can result from mild to severe acute COVID-19 among all ages, with the largest prevalence among people ages 36–50, and with most cases occurring among people who had not been hospitalized with COVID-19 (FAIR Health, 2022). Rates of Long COVID among those contracting COVID-19 vary from 10 percent to 30 percent, depending on the study (Brown et al., 2022), with conservative estimates at 10 percent (Davis et al., 2023) and risk increasing with COVID-19 reinfections (Koumoundouros, 2023), especially for older adults (Boufidou et al., 2023). In 2022, the National Center for Health Statistics reported that 7.5 percent of Americans had Long COVID, with one in five who had COVID-19 reporting they developed Long COVID (National Center for Health Statistics, 2022). It is estimated that 63 million people worldwide have Long COVID (Davis et al., 2023), and it is confirmed now that Long COVID can be disabling and last for years (Davis et al., 2023; Li et al., 2023). The HHS Office of Civil Rights (2021) and the U.S. Department of Justice Civil Rights Division advised that Long COVID qualifies as a disability under the Americans with Disabilities Act. As a result, and not surprisingly, the number of people with disabilities in the United States has been climbing since June 2021 (U.S. Bureau of Labor Statistics, 2024), with Long COVID being identified by some as a likely mass-disabling event for the U.S. labor market (Choo & Kominers, 2023; Edwards, 2022). This concern is amplified, given that the most recent wave of COVID-19 infections in January 2024 surpassed the January 2022 Omicron wave (Paris, 2024). Even though severe illness is much less frequent (Paris, 2024), one needs to remain cognizant of the research that repeat infections increase the risk of Long COVID and that the majority of Long COVID cases resulted from mild infections.

While an increase in people with disabilities is clearly a concern for social work simply because of the need to provide services and to advocate with and for people with disabilities, it is also becoming clear that Long COVID needs to be a broader concern because it has significantly strained the health care workforce (Ready, 2023). For example, in Brazil, a study of healthcare personnel identified a 27 percent rate of Long COVID among those who contracted COVID-19, with multiple infections increasing the risk (Marra et al., 2023). Not unexpectedly, when healthcare workers get Long COVID, many find that it affects their ability to continue working. For example, among UK doctors with Long COVID, almost one in five (18 percent) identified being unable to work due to Long COVID, and of those who were working, one in three said they were unable to work full-time (British Medical Association, 2023; Sibonney, 2023). More studies are needed: We were unable to locate any major studies of Long COVID among the U.S. healthcare workforce (or the social work workforce). However, the University at Buffalo School of Social Work's podcast series *inSocialWork* featured an episode focusing on the experience of a social worker with Long COVID, and a discussion on some of the implications for social work practice (Sobota, 2023). This appears to be an exception in the profession at present.

Many people with Long COVID are facing stigma and social denial of the plight of those with that condition (Yong, 2023). These issues, combined with complaints of "medical gaslighting" and challenges in accessing care (Au et al., 2022), highlight the urgent need for increased attention from social workers. Simultaneously, we must be cognizant of the impact of Long COVID within our own profession in all domains and at all levels of practice, including in social work education. The latter is noteworthy, given that Long COVID has been found at significant levels (30 percent) in students, faculty, and staff in at least one university (Landry et al., 2023). This fact points to the need for further research on the impact of Long COVID on the social work workforce and profession.

ADVOCACY GROUPS

Advocacy groups have filled the void left by international, national, state, and local public health interventions and public policy mandates. While prevalence of the virus is generally reported by the Centers for Disease Control and Prevention (CDC) in hospitalizations and deaths, advocacy groups online and in print have noted that these figures underestimate the prevalence of viral spread. With testing centers largely replaced by home testing kits, advocates have encouraged the following of wastewater surveillance methods (CDC, 2023a, 2023b) as a better predictor for the need to use public health measures (although it should be noted that these data do not cover septic tanks). Body Politic, Survivor Corps, Long COVID Alliance, Long COVID Families, Long COVID Kids, People's CDC, and covidCAREgroup, for example, have been lifelines to those concerned about what to do with COVID infections—initial and Long COVID—and more importantly how to manage the fragmentation of care and locate, manage, and interface with the public health and medical establishment. They also have led research collaborations (Patient-Led Research Collaborative, n.d.) that, along with concerned medical professionals, have made significant inroads into understanding what is happening on the ground.

CONCLUSION

Understanding the multitude of policy and practice implications brought on by the COVID-19 pandemic and its postviral conditions (i.e., Long COVID) is imperative for social workers. The profession also has an obligation to develop research into the effects of the pandemic on social workers' physical health and well-being, form alliances with other health professionals to fill the gap in informed health messaging, and understand the ongoing impacts of the virus on society at multiple levels of social work practice. Regardless of whether one believes that the pandemic is over, the long-term effects on health, societal fabric, or community life are not behind us, rather we are just now beginning to understand that COVID-19 and Long COVID will be with us for a very long time. Taken together, this points to the need for increased attention in all our educational institutions, professional organizations, and research initiatives to address these ongoing public health concerns. **HSW**

REFERENCES

Agergaard, J., Gunst, J. D., Schiøttz-Christensen, B., Østergaard, L., & Wejse, C. (2023). Long-term prognosis at 1.5 years after infection with wild-type strain of SARS-CoV-2 and Alpha, Delta, as well as Omicron variants. *International Journal of Infectious Disease, 137*, 126–133. https://doi.org/10.1016/j.ijid.2023.10.022

AJMC. (2021, January 1). *A timeline for COVID-19 developments in 2020.* https://www.ajmc.com/view/a-timeline-of-covid19-developments-in-2020

Au, L., Capotescu, C., Eyal, G., & Finestone, G. (2022). Long Covid and medical gaslighting: Dismissal, delayed diagnosis, and deferred treatment. *SSM – Qualitative Research in Health, 2*, Article 100167. https://doi.org/10.1016/j.ssmqr.2022.100167

Bonotti, M., & Zech, S. T. (2021). *Recovering civility during COVID-19.* https://doi.org/10.1007/978-981-33-6706-7_1

Boufidou, F., Medić, S., Lampropoulou, V., Siafakas, N., Tsakris, A., & Anastassopoulou, C. (2023). SARS-CoV-2 reinfections and long COVID in the post-Omicron phase of the pandemic. *International Journal of Molecular Science, 24,* Article 12962. https://doi.org/10.3390/ijms241612962

British Medical Association. (2023, July 4). *First major survey of doctors with Long Covid reveals debilitating impact on health, life and work.* https://www.bma.org.uk/bma-media-centre/first-major-survey-of-doctors-with-long-covid-reveals-debilitating-impact-on-health-life-and-work-and-wider-implications-for-workforce-and-health-services

Brown, H., Fremsted, S., & Tache, J. (2022, December 20). *The extent and demographics of Long COVID disability in the United States.* Center for Economic and Policy Research. https://cepr.net/the-extent-and-demographics-of-long-covid-disability-in-united-states/

Burns, A. (2022, August 1). *What are the implications of long COVID for employment and health coverage.* Kaiser Family Foundation. https://www.kff.org/policy-watch/what-are-the-implications-of-long-covid-for-employment-and-health-coverage/

CBS News. (2022, September 19). *Biden says COVID-19 pandemic is "over" in U.S.* https://www.cbsnews.com/news/biden-covid-pandemic-over/

Centers for Disease Control and Prevention. (2023a). *Long Covid or Post-Covid conditions.* https://www.cdc.gov/coronavirus/2019-ncov/long-term-effects/index.html

Centers for Disease Control and Prevention. (2023b). *National Wastewater Surveillance System.* https://www.cdc.gov/nwss/wastewater-surveillance.html

Choo, E. K., & Kominers, S. D. (2023, April 5). We need an Operation Warp Speed for long COVID. *Scientific American.* https://www.scientificamerican.com/article/we-need-an-operation-warp-speed-for-long-covid/

Columbia University Mailman School of Public Health. (2021, February 19). *Epidemic, endemic, pandemic: What are the differences?* https://www.publichealth.columbia.edu/news/epidemic-endemic-pandemic-what-are-differences

Cubanski, J., Kates, J., Tolbert, J., Guth, M., Pollitz, K., & Freed, M. (2023, January 31). *What happens when COVID-19 emergency declarations end? Implications for coverage, costs, and access.* Kaiser Family Foundation. https://www.kff.org/coronavirus-covid-19/issue-brief/what-happens-when-covid-19-emergency-declarations-end-implications-for-coverage-costs-and-access/

Davis, H. E., McCorkell, L., Vogel, J. M., & Topol, E. J. (2023). Long COVID: Major findings, mechanisms and recommendations. *Nature Reviews: Microbiology, 21,* 133–146. https://doi.org/10.1038/s41579-022-00846-2

De Wit, J. B. F., de Ridder, D. T. D., van den Boom, W., Kroese, F. M., van den Putte, B., Stok, F. M., Leurs, M., & de Bruin, M. (2023). Understanding public support for COVID-19 pandemic mitigation measures over time: Does it wear out? *Frontiers in Public Health, 11,* Article 1079992. https://doi.org/10.3389/fpubh.2023.1079992

Du, M., Ma, Y., Deng, J., Liu, M., & Liu, J. (2022). Comparison of long COVID-19 caused by different SARS-CoV-2 strains: A systematic review and meta-analysis. *International Journal of Environmental Research and Public Health, 19,* Article 16010. https://doi.org/10.3390/ijerph192316010

Edwards, K. A. (2022, December 7). *Long COVID is a mass disability. The labor market is in denial* [Commentary]. Rand. https://www.rand.org/pubs/commentary/2022/12/long-covid-is-a-mass-disability-the-labor-market-is.html

European Centre for Disease Prevention and Control. (2024, February 5). *SARS-CoV-2 variants of concern as of 2 February 2024.* https://www.ecdc.europa.eu/en/covid-19/variants-concern

FAIR Health. (2022, May 19). *FAIR Health releases study on post-COVID conditions.* http://www.fairhealth.org/article/fair-health-releases-study-on-post-covid-conditions

Freckelton, I. (2020). COVID-19: Fear, quackery, false representations and the law. *International Journal of Law and Psychiatry, 72,* Article 101611. https://doi.org/10.1016/j.ijlp.2020.101611

Gulumbe, B. H., & Yusuf, Z. M. (2023). The World Health Organization's post-pandemic stance: What does it mean for global health? [Letter to the Editor]. *Public Health Research & Practice, 33,* Article e3322318. https://doi.org/10.17061/phrp3322318

International Monetary Fund. (2020, June). *Six prominent thinkers reflect on how the pandemic has changed the world.* https://www.imf.org/en/Publications/fandd/issues/2020/06/how-will-the-world-be-different-after-COVID-19

Jee Y. (2020). WHO international health regulations emergency committee for the COVID-19 outbreak. *Epidemiology and Health, 42,* Article e2020013.

Kelly, H. (2011). The classical definition of a pandemic is not elusive. *Bulletin of the World Health Organization, 89,* 540–541. https://doi.org/10.2471/BLT.11.088815

Koumoundouros, T. (2023, December 26). *Every COVID infection increases your risk of long COVID, study warns.* ScienceAlert. https://www.sciencealert.com/every-covid-infection-increases-your-risk-of-long-covid-study-warns

Kupferschmidt, K., & Wadman, M. (2023, May 5). 'It's still killing and it's still changing.' Ending COVID-19 states of emergency sparks debate. *Science, 380,* 566–567. https://doi.org/10.1126/science.adi6511

Landry, M., Bornstein, S., Nagaraj, N., Sardon, G. A., Castel, A., Vyas, A., McDonnell, K., Agneshwar, M., Wilkinson, A., & Goldman, L. (2023). Postacute sequelae of SARS-CoV-2 in university setting. *Emerging Infectious Diseases, 29,* 519–527. https://doi.org/10.3201/eid2903.221522

Li, J., Zhou, Y., Ma, J., Zhang, Q., Shao, J., Liang, S., Yu, Y., Li, W., & Wang, C. (2023). The long-term health outcomes, pathophysiological mechanisms and multidisciplinary management of long COVID. *Signal Transduction and Targeted Therapy, 8,* Article 416. https://doi.org/10.1038/s41392-023-01640-z

Marra, A. R., Sampaio, V. S., Ozahata, M. C., Lopes, R., Brito, A. F., Bragatte, M., Kalil, J., Miraglia, J. L., Malheiro, D. T., Guozhang, Y., Teich, V. D., Victor, E. da S., Pinho, J. R. R., Cypriano, A., Vieira, L. W., Polonio, M., de Oliveira, S. M., Ricardo, V. C. V., Maezato, A. M., . . . Rizzo, L. V. (2023). Risk factors for long coronavirus disease 2019 (long COVID) among healthcare personnel, Brazil, 2020-2022. *Infection Control & Hospital Epidemiology, 44,* 1972–1978. https://doi.org/10.1017/ice.2023.95

McNeely, C. L., & Schintler, L. A. (2020). The pandemic challenge: Reflections on the social justice dynamic. *World Medical & Health Policy, 12,* 344–346. https://doi.org/10.1002/wmh3.375

National Academies of Sciences, Engineering, and Medicine. (2022). *Long COVID: Examining long-term health effects of COVID-19 and implications for the Social Security*

Administration: Proceedings of a workshop. National Academies Press. https://doi.org/10.17226/26619

National Center for Health Statistics. (2022, June 22). *Nearly one in five American adults who have had COVID-19 still have "long COVID."* https://www.cdc.gov/nchs/press room/nchs_press_releases/2022/20220622.htm

Northwestern Institute for Policy Research. (2023, April 12). *Survey: Is the CDC missing the mark on vaccination rates?* https://www.ipr.northwestern.edu/news/2023/survey-is-the-cdc-missing-the-mark-on-vacci nation-rates.html

Otto, S. P., Day, T., Arino, J., Colijn, C., Dushoff, J., Li, M., Mechai, S., Van Domselaar, G., Wu, J., Earn, D. J. D., & Ogden, N. H. (2021). The origins and potential future of SARS-CoV-2 variants of concern in the evolving COVID-19 pandemic. *Current Biology, 31*, R918–R929. https://doi.org/10.1016/j.cub.2021.06.049

Paris, F. (2024, January 10). We are in a big COVID wave. But just how big? *New York Times.* https://www.nytimes .com/2024/01/10/upshot/covid-pandemic-wave.html

Patient-Led Research Collaborative. (n.d.). *About the Patient-Led Research Collaborative.* Retrieved February 4, 2024, from https://patientresearchcovid19.com/

Ratzan, S. C., Gostin, L. O., Meshkati, N., Rabin, K., & Parker, R. M. (2020, March 5). *COVID-19: An urgent call for coordinated, trusted sources to tell everyone what they need to know and do* [Commentary]. National Academy of Medicine. https://doi.org/10.31478/202003a

Ready, T. (2023, March 6). *Long COVID takes toll on already stretched health care workforce.* WebMD. https://www.webmd.com/covid/news/20230306/long-covid-takes-toll-on-health-care-system

Sibonney, C. (2023, August 31). *One in 5 doctors with Long COVID can no longer work: Survey.* Medscape. https://www.medscape.com/viewarticle/996030?icd=login_success_email_match_norm

Sobota, P. (Host). (2023, September 19). Long COVID and the implications for social work [Audio podcast episode]. In *inSocialWork.* University at Buffalo, School of Social Work. https://www.insocialwork.org/long-covid-and-the-implications-for-so cial-work/

Social Security Administration. (2023, June). *Long COVID: A guideline for health professionals on providing medical evidence for social security disability claims* (Publication No. 64-128). https://www.ssa.gov/disability/professio nals/documents/EN-64-128.pdf

Stephenson, J. (2022, April 12). Biden administration outlines strategy to tackle long covid. *JAMA Health Forum, 3,* Article e221280. https://doi.org/10.1001/jamahealthforum.2022.1280

Tyson, A., & Funk, C. (2022, February 9). *Increasing public criticism over COVID-19 response.* Pew Research Center. https://www.pewresearch.org/science/2022/02/09/increasing-public-criticism-confusion-over-covid-19-response-in-u-s/

U.S. Bureau of Labor Statistics. (2024, February 2). *Population—With a disability, 16 years and over.* Federal Reserve Bank of St. Louis. https://fred.stlouisfed.org/series/LNU00074597

U.S. Department of Health and Human Services. (n.d.). *About Long COVID.* Retrieved February 4, 2024, from https://www.covid.gov/be-informed/longco vid/about

U.S. Department of Health and Human Services, Administration for Strategic Preparedness and Response. (2020, January 31). *Determination that a public health emergency exists nationwide as the result of the 2019 novel coronavirus* [PHE declaration]. https://aspr.hhs.gov/le gal/PHE/Pages/2019-nCoV.aspx

U.S. Department of Health and Human Services, Office of Civil Rights. (2021, July 26). *Guidance on "long COVID" as disability under the ADA, Section 504, and Section 1557.* https://www.hhs.gov/civil-rights/for-pro viders/civil-rights-covid19/guidance-long-covid-dis ability/index.html

Vales, F. (2023, May 2). *COVID-19 is still a thing in 2023, and here is why you should care.* Youth Engaged 4 Change. https://engage.youth.gov/blog/covid-19-still-thing-2023-and-heres-why-you-should-care

White House. (2023, April 10). *Press briefing by Press Secretary Karine Jean Pierre and National Security Council for Strategic Communications John Kirby.* https://www .whitehouse.gov/briefing-room/legislation/2023/04/10/bill-signed-h-j-res-7/

White House, Executive Office of the President. (2020, March 18). *Proclamation 9994: Declaring a national emergency concerning the novel coronavirus disease (COVID-19) outbreak* (Presidential Document No. 2020-05794). *Federal Register, 85,* 15337–15338. https://www .govinfo.gov/content/pkg/FR-2020-03-18/pdf/2020-05794.pdf

Williams, M. A. (2022, September 27). Op-ed: Biden's premature declaration on the end of the COVID-19 pandemic. *HSPH News.* https://www.hsph.harvard .edu/news/hsph-in-the-news/biden-premature-dec laration-on-end-of-covid-19-pandemic/

World Health Organization. (n.d.). *Coronavirus disease (COVID-19) pandemic.* Retrieved December 18, 2023, from https://www.who.int/europe/emergen cies/situations/covid-19

World Health Organization. (2023, May 5). *Statement of the fifteenth meeting of the IHR (2005) Emergency Committee on the COVID-19 pandemic.* https://www.who.int/news/item/05-05-2023-statement-on-the-fifteenth-meeting-of-the-international-health-regulations-(2005)-emergency-committee-regarding-the-corona virus-disease-(covid-19)-pandemic

Yong, E. (2023, April 19). Long COVID is being erased—again. *The Atlantic.* https://www.theatlantic.com/health/archive/2023/04/long-covid-symptoms-invis ible-disability-chronic-illness/673773/

Susan A. Taylor, PhD, MSW, *is professor, School of Social Work, California State University, Sacramento, 6000 J Street, Sacramento, CA 95819-6090, USA; email: taylors@csus.edu.* **Nancy J. Smyth, PhD, MSW, LCSW,** *is professor and associate dean for faculty development, School of Social Work, University at Buffalo, Buffalo, NY, USA.*

Original manuscript received February 7, 2024
Editorial decision February 12, 2024
Accepted February 9, 2024
Advance Access Publication April 8, 2024

ECONOMIC
Well-Being

AN INTRODUCTION

DEBORAH M. FIGART
and ELLEN MUTARI

We are all part of the economy. We all have contributions to make to the economic well-being of our communities. We all make decisions about how we conduct our economic lives based on our values and preferences. *Economic Well-Being: An Introduction* provides us with tools to accomplish these goals.

As students of social work or other human services professions, it is essential that we understand how economic well-being—or the lack thereof—shapes people's lives. To use a person-in-environment framework, we must appreciate the challenges faced by our clients, including their access to financial resources and their level of economic functioning. In this groundbreaking text, Figart and Mutari make the study of economic life accessible, applicable, and exciting.

ISBN: 978-0-87101-580-8 • 2022
Item #5808 • 304 pages
1-800-227-3590 • www.naswpress.org

NASW PRESS

NASW
National Association of Social Workers

APEWB22

Black Alaskans Health Needs Assessment during COVID-19 Pandemic: Implications for Social Work

Amana Mbise, Celeste Hodge-Growden, Thea Bemben, and Rei Shimizu

At the peak of the COVID-19 pandemic it became clear that Black people were experiencing more severe symptoms and had higher rates of mortality from COVID-19 than White people. However, data on racial differences in death and hospitalization rates in Alaska were less clear. To address this, the Alaska Black Caucus initiated the first Black Alaskans health needs assessment to understand the health status, needs, and resources of the Black community of Alaska. This article reports on the design, implementation, and descriptive results from the survey portion of the first community health needs assessment of Black Alaskans. The findings indicate that a majority of Black Alaskans report being moderately healthy, having access to health insurance, owning their homes, and having a favorable view of their neighborhood. However, too many are unable to work due to poor physical or mental health challenges and are diagnosed with one or more chronic health diseases. In addition, Black Alaskans experience high rates of substance abuse, have untreated mental health conditions, consume tobacco products at a high rate, and are not screening for some cancers. The article will conclude by presenting additional strategies for improving healthcare access and responsiveness for Black Alaskans.

KEY WORDS: *Black Alaskans; community health needs assessment; health disparities*

COVID-19 has made a disproportionate social impact on Black people and other racial minorities in Alaska. However, data on racial differences in death and hospitalization rates are less clear. As of July 2021, approximately 34 percent of all Alaska's COVID-19 cases were labeled as "unknown race," "under investigation," "multiple races," or "other race." Such ambiguous categorization prevents understanding of the full impact of COVID-19 on the Black community and, in turn, complicates efforts to accurately identify and address health issues that Black Alaskans experience.

In light of these issues, the Alaska Black Caucus (ABC)—the largest and oldest agency championing the constitutional rights of Black people in the state of Alaska—applied for and received funding from the Anchorage Health Department to conduct a community health needs assessment in order to document the health status and needs of Black Alaskans during the COVID-19 pandemic. To our knowledge, this was the first community health needs assessment of Black Alaskans and the first undertaken by a minority-led organization. The project incorporates a community-focused research approach as a way of obtaining health-related input from Black Alaskans. This article reports on the design, implementation, and descriptive results from the survey portion of the assessment and illuminates the health status and needs of the Black community. It will conclude by presenting additional strategies for improving healthcare access and responsiveness for Black Alaskans.

THE ABC

Founded in 1975, the ABC is a membership-based organization committed to championing the rights of Black Alaskans in the areas of education, justice, health, and economics. Members of the ABC come from diverse backgrounds, forming a multiethnic and multicultural alliance for justice and equity. The ABC has extensive experience collaborating with community stakeholders to conduct community-led programs to advance the health and well-being of Black Alaskans.

ABC's work operates through committees focused on education, health, justice, economics, and youth. At the core of this work is a commitment to developing community-based programs that align with the local needs of the Black community of Alaska. Such programs have included community advocacy, equity-based organizational trainings, community forums, health fairs, and ballot initiatives. The ABC is also committed to living the legacy of Bettye Davis, the first African American Senator in Alaska. The annual Bettye Davis African American Summit, among other things, seeks to highlight issues affecting the Black community of Alaska and engaging with policymakers and the public to create lasting solutions. During the COVID-19 pandemic, the ABC became an important partner in the rollout of vaccinations, outreach, and community health education for the Black community of Alaska.

CONTEXT OF THE BLACK ALASKANS HEALTH NEEDS ASSESSMENT
Black in Alaska

For over 150 years, Black people have called Alaska their home where they actively participate in the politics, economic development, and culture of the state (Hartman, 2021). Their influence grew over the decades, and today people who identify as Black make up an important part of the population of Alaska. According to the 2020 U.S. census data, the share of the population of Alaska that identifies as Black grew from 2.8 percent to 3.4 percent in the last 10 years (U.S. Census Bureau, n.d.).

The Black community of Alaska is diverse. For the purposes of this assessment, the Black community included those who identify as African American or people of the Black diaspora, which includes foreign-born Black people who either voluntarily or involuntarily migrated to the United States.

Problems Documenting Health Needs

Despite this growing share of the Black population in Alaska and the contributions of Black people to the political, cultural, and economic life of the state, Black people remain marginalized, experience racism, and bear high levels of health disparities. At the height of the COVID-19 pandemic, Black people in Alaska—as in the rest of the United States—were experiencing higher rates of illness and death (Golden, 2020). At the same time, the American Public Health Association (APHA) and the Centers for Disease Control and Prevention (CDC), following declarations at various state and local levels, declared racism a public health issue that negatively impacts social determinants of health and creates barriers to health equity among Black people, even though eliminating health disparities remains an overarching goal of *Healthy People 2030* (APHA, 2021; Office of Disease Prevention and Health Promotion, n.d.).

In the face of a growing consensus that solutions to health inequities require grounding in data, the *Healthy People 2030* goals clearly state that "measuring health disparities is essential to advancing health equity" (Office of Disease Prevention and Health Promotion, n.d., para. 7). Such measures should unmask the disproportionate burden and toll of disease that marginalized communities, like Black communities, bear. However, municipal and state health data from Alaska reveal the absence of adequate documentation of the toll of COVID and other illnesses within the Alaskan Black community since large gaps persist in reporting based on race and ethnicity.

Rationale for the Black Alaskans Health Needs Assessment

Solutions to address health inequities should be developed by and for the affected communities. This is a core principle of community-focused health research (Awad et al., 2022; Smalley et al., 2021) that legitimizes community engagement in health policymaking. So, while the ABC initiated the community health needs assessment, it was largely a collective community effort. Five community partners rotated to offer input to guide the assessment's design, implementation, and dissemination. Reflecting best practice, community health needs assessments incorporate the principles of community-engaged research (CER), which is a "process of working collaboratively with groups of people affiliated by geographic proximity, special interests, or similar situations with respect to issues affecting their well-being" (U.S. Department of Health and Human Services, 2011, p. 3). CER reflects a paradigm shift in conducting research that integrates minoritized voices and communities of color as equal collaborators in the face of social forces limiting involvement through majoritarian institutions (Payán et al., 2022). This assessment fulfills two main principles of CER, as it was in direct response to a community request for conducting a health needs assessment and involved members of the affected community.

Community-engaged assessments are vital to identifying the health concerns of communities and their members, largely those of minoritized groups. Learning about factors that influence members of minoritized groups' health needs, status, and resources/assets is an advantage of community-engaged assessments (Grant et al., 2015). Since these assessments shift away from deficit models to emphasize existing community assets, resources, and knowledge, they present strategic opportunities to promote health equity within low-income communities and communities of color (Ward et al., 2018). Such engagement can offset mistrust among those community-engaged members who may see mainstream institutions as exploitive and neglectful of the needs of minoritized groups.

Community-engaged assessments incorporate collaborative partnerships between researchers and community partners to address health risk factors and strengths in the community. Community-engaged assessments seek to address multiple determinants of health that are important to communities (Israel et al., 2010). In addition, linking research to action is central to community-engaged assessments. For instance, Garcia-Rivera et al. (2017) focus on the use of community health needs assessments by creating a participatory action plan to reduce health disparities among rural Puerto Ricans. This commitment to action and involving stakeholders makes community-engaged assessments especially appropriate for addressing disparate health outcomes in communities of color that result from inequitable distribution of economic, political, environmental, and social resources (Payán et al., 2022; Ward et al., 2018).

Implementing the Black Alaskans Health Needs Assessment

In 2021, the ABC called for researchers who could help design and implement the first Black Alaskans health needs assessment. This is central to CER: The project originates from a community's outreach to researchers to facilitate and implement an assessment agenda emanating from community leaders, which is in stark contrast to researcher-initiated projects (Balls-Berry & Acosta-Pérez, 2017; Buckingham et al., 2022).

The ABC's motivation was driven by a persistent lack of health data specific to the Black community of Alaska. In addition, it sought to adopt a health-affirming, nonpathologizing perspective to understand the health needs, status, and resources

of the Black community of Alaska. In this sense, the initiation of the assessment within the community added to the health activism of the ABC as a principal advocacy organization within the state. Propelling the assessment, therefore, was an advocacy agenda rather than a research agenda alone.

Before the assessment could commence and to ensure that the assessment was community-driven, the ABC formed a community steering team comprising members from ABC and the community and researchers from the University of Alaska Anchorage. The community steering team devised strategies to engage diverse members of the Black community in a culturally affirming manner and provided social capital for connecting with data sources within that community. This important first step allowed the community steering team to ensure the representation of perspectives and voices throughout the process. Beyond representation, the community steering team was central in designing the assessment. For instance, it was important for them to have a clear and agreed-upon understanding of the diverse groups composing the Black community of Alaska. It was through team deliberations in conjunction with the input of ABC members that the community steering team agreed to take in anyone who identified as African American or Black, including those who had Black as one of their primary identities among others.

The Anchorage Health Department helped with identifying relevant datasets for analysis and the largest church in Anchorage serving a diverse congregation was integral to outreach to the Black community and served as a venue for conducting focus group discussions.

Community partners were also important for establishing trust among members of the Black community of Alaska. Utilizing the ABC for outreach in the community helped the community steering team to gain trust and encourage members of the Black community to complete surveys, participate in focus group discussions, and dissemination efforts. This was important as the ABC holds considerable trust within the Black community earned through its own outreach and community health education initiatives.

The design of the assessment, in large part, relied on the long-standing trusting relationships between the school of social work and community partners. The members of the community steering team were of different racial and ethnic backgrounds, forming a multiracial collaboration that brought together diverse personal and professional experiences and expertise to the assessment. The legitimacy of the project was strengthened because the leader of the ABC was deeply embedded, respected, and trusted within the Black community of Alaska.

METHOD
Design
The project's multipronged approach to understanding the health status and needs of Black Alaskans enabled the achievement of the following aims: (a) capturing Black Alaskans' perspective of their health and well-being, (b) highlighting the challenges that Black people in Alaska face in protecting and advancing their health, and (c) setting the stage for subsequent action by the ABC to advance the health of the Black community of Alaska. The assessment incorporated three parts: (1) secondary analysis of publicly available population health data examining the health status of Black Alaskans in relation to other racial and ethnic groups in Alaska and the United States, (2) primary data collection through an online survey and interviews, and (3) building community awareness of the health needs of Black Alaskans.

Sample and Sampling
The steering team planned to select a minimum of 300 adult Alaskans who identified as Black. All Black Alaskans who were 18 years of age or older and located in remote and urban Alaska were eligible for inclusion in the assessment. Convenience sampling was used to recruit participants through social media and posters displayed in public spaces. The posters contained information about the assessment, a link, and a QR code for the survey. To ensure greater participation and engagement, we utilized the ABC's social media platforms (Facebook and Twitter) as well as targeted public spaces where Black Alaskans congregate, such as Shiloh Ministry Baptist Church. As a result, our final sample size was 675, which is approximately 2.5 percent of the Black population of Alaska.

Measures
We used the CDC Behavioral Risk Factor Surveillance System Questionnaire (BRFSS) to inform our health assessment. The questionnaire contained 76 items and indicators of community health status categorized under Healthy Communities, General Health Status of Individuals, Health Behaviors, Healthcare Services, Access and Coverage, Demographic Characteristics, and Housing and Neighborhood Characteristics. The questionnaire was distributed via a secure, university-issued Qualtrics account. The survey took approximately 40–60 minutes to complete.

For the qualitative portion, a semistructured interview guide was implemented for both focus groups and individual key informant interviews. The guide contained open-ended questions following the results of the survey on the perception of health by Black Alaskans, challenges to accessing healthcare, and recommendations for improving the health and well-being of the Black community of Alaska.

Data Collection
Primary data were collected through an online survey, focus group discussions, and key informant interviews. Participants could complete the survey on their smartphones, tablets, and personal or public computers. Collecting data through an online survey was deemed most appropriate to mitigate against the spread of COVID-19 virus. It was also logistically easier to reach people in remote areas of Alaska. Once all data were collected, they were exported to SPSS software for statistical analysis. The survey was followed by focus group discussions and key informant interviews. Because of COVID-19, all interviews were held online through Zoom videoconference tool. This manuscript reports specifically on the descriptive analysis of the quantitative survey.

Secondary data collection involved an analysis of publicly available health data from 1996 to 2022 to understand indicators of morbidity; mortality; and maternal, infant, and child health by race comparing Black Alaskans with White Alaskans, American Indian/Alaska Native people, and the general U.S. population. The sources of the secondary data included CDC WONDER database, National Violent Death Reporting System, Alaska Vital Statistics, Alaska Behavioral Risk Factor Surveillance System, Alaska Department of Maternal Child Death Review Program, and the Alaska Maternal and Child Health Data Books. This manuscript will report specifically on the findings from the primary data analysis. The findings from the secondary data analysis were reported separately (Shimizu et al., 2022).

Data Analysis

Once collected, the data were entered into SPSS (Version 28) for statistical analysis. Descriptive statistics were then computed to get a sense of the distribution of data for all variables and to identify the main issues affecting the health and status of Black Alaskans.

RESULTS

Sociodemographics of Sample

Table 1 summarizes the sociodemographic characteristics of participants in the survey. The majority of participants identified as male (56 percent), were between the ages of 35 and 44 (38 percent), were married (70 percent), had a technical or trade school certificate (18 percent), had a household income between $50,000 and $74,999 (38 percent), and worked in a job or owned a business (83 percent).

General Health Status

Most participants perceive the health of the Black community of Alaska as being good and moderately healthy. The leading health problems in the community are hypertension (24 percent), overweight (23 percent), alcohol abuse (24 percent), depression (23 percent), high cholesterol (19 percent), mental health issues (24 percent), substance abuse (19 percent), and arthritis/rheumatism (20 percent). About 33 percent indicated that they lose a day or two of work due to poor physical or mental health.

Health Behaviors

The majority of participants (80 percent) engage in moderate activities or exercise at least three to four times a week, and nearly 40 percent are trying to lose weight. Forty percent consume two to three alcoholic drinks every week, 24 percent consume four to five, 10 percent consume six or more, and 20 percent do not consume alcohol. Nearly 60 percent of participants consume tobacco products including cigarettes, pipe tobacco, and cigars; 43 percent indicated that they do not plan to quit smoking within the next six months.

Regarding fruit and vegetable consumption, 95 percent of participants indicated that they eat, on average, one or more servings of fruit each day (excluding juices), and about 50 percent consume three to four servings of vegetables daily. Another 38 percent consume one to two servings of vegetables daily, while roughly 3 percent do not eat any servings of vegetables daily.

In the past year, 55 participants received a flu shot, 36 percent had a colorectal cancer screening, 33 percent had their teeth cleaned by a dentist or dental hygienist, and 33 percent visited the dentist or dental clinic for any reason. Likewise, 11 percent have never had a blood sugar test for diabetes, 12 percent have never had skin or other cancer screening, and 5 percent have never had a routine checkup by a doctor or health provider.

In terms of screening for cancer, 14 percent of participants have never had a mammogram, 13 percent have never had a clinical breast exam, and 14 percent have never had a Papanicolaou test for cervical cancer. For men, 16 percent report that they have never screened for prostate cancer or rectal exam.

Nearly 73 percent of participants indicated that all their children, or those in their households, were up to date on their immunization shot while 1 percent said they do not know the status of their children's immunizations. Some of the reasons for not getting their children immunized include: "can't get time off work" (15 percent), "didn't know they had to be immunized" (15 percent), "no health insurance" (13 percent), "no provider" (19 percent), "too expensive" (10 percent), "against my religious beliefs" (8 percent), "don't think it's important" (7 percent), and "other reasons" (2 percent).

Neighborhood Factors and Access to Care

In terms of neighborhood factors and access to care, nearly 50 percent of participants reside in apartment-type homes, followed by single-family homes (24 percent) and condo/townhouses (23 percent). Over half own their homes (58 percent), and 50 percent have a favorable view of their neighborhood.

Twenty-four percent said their neighborhood offers easy, walkable access to public outdoor spaces, while 23 percent describe their neighborhood as having easy access to health food stores and restaurants. Another 24 percent see their neighborhood as environmentally safe providing clean air and water, while 23 percent say that they feel safe with little or low crime occurrences. About 19 percent say that their neighborhood location provides access to good quality schools.

Table 1: Sociodemographics of the Sample (N = 675)			
Sociodemographic Characteristic	**Range**	**n (%)**	**Missing n (%)**
Gender			44 (6)
Male		379 (56)	
Female		250 (37)	
Nonbinary/third gender		1 (0.1)	
Prefer not to say		1 (0.1)	
Age (years)	35–44	258 (38)	44 (6)
Marital status			45 (7)
Married (including common law)		474 (70)	
Separated		15 (2)	
Divorced		15 (2)	
Widowed		3 (0.4)	
Single		118 (18)	
Prefer not to say		5 (0.7)	
Highest level of education			47 (7)
Some high school (no diploma)		20 (3)	
High school diploma/GED		90 (13)	
Some college (no degree)		117 (17)	
Technical or trade school certificate		124 (18)	
Associate's degree		117 (17)	
Bachelor's degree		109 (16)	
Master's degree		46 (7)	
Doctoral degree		5 (0.7)	
Born in the United States			46 (6.8)
Yes		513 (76)	
No		116 (17)	
Use language other than English			47 (7)
Yes		87 (14)	
No		533 (79)	
Current occupation			48 (7)
Working in a job or owning a business		558 (83)	
Looking for work		35 (5)	
Student		17 (3)	
Retired		10 (2)	
Stay-at-home partner or spouse		3 (0.4)	
Household income ($)	50,000–74,999	255 (38)	

Nearly half (46 percent) do not have a mental health provider that they see regularly. Out of those with a mental health provider, 40 percent reported that they most recently saw their provider for counseling/therapy, hospitalization (24 percent), crisis care (21 percent), and other mental health services (33 percent).

A majority (83 percent) report having health insurance, of which 57 percent have health insurance through their employer or private provider, 36 percent are on Medicare or Medicaid, 3 percent have health insurance through the Tribal Health Services, and 3 percent have health insurance through the military or the U.S. Department of Veterans Affairs. Despite this high rate of coverage, a majority (61 percent) could not receive the care they needed due to cost and other financial factors; could not get appointments (56 percent); provider was not available (48 percent); or the provider would not accept their health insurance (52 percent). The reasons for not having health insurance included inability to afford premiums (7.8 percent), job loss due to COVID-19 or change in employment (7.5 percent), and divorce or separation (1.7 percent).

In summary, a majority of Black Alaskans view themselves as moderately healthy, have access to health insurance, own their homes, and have a favorable view of their neighborhoods. Some are practicing healthy eating habits such as consuming fruits, getting flu shots, actively seeking to lose weight, and adopting preventive health behaviors including screening for cancer at least once in their lifetime. On the other hand, too many are unable to work due to poor physical health or mental illness; are diagnosed with one or more chronic health diseases; experience high rates of substance abuse; have untreated mental health conditions; consume tobacco products at a high rate; and experience barriers to accessing care due to high costs, underinsurance, lack of information, and a lack of healthcare providers in the state of Alaska.

DISCUSSION

The first Black Alaskans health needs assessment shows the many health issues that Black Alaskans are facing. It also demonstrates the importance of community partnerships in advancing health in underserved communities. Partnerships that draw on the expertise and diverse perspectives of community stakeholders such as community-based agencies, academic researchers, faith-based institutions, and health providers have been shown to be effective in promoting health in low-income and marginalized communities (Belgrave et al., 2021). Specifically, they have been shown to be effective in reducing cardiometabolic risk among African American women (Villablanca et al., 2016) and increased fruit and vegetable intake in rural African American communities (Barnidge et al., 2015).

Furthermore, despite Black Alaskans having health insurance, incomes that are above national averages, and above-average home ownership rates, the assessment has shown that many are unable to receive the care they need due to high costs, high premiums, and underinsurance. This may also point to the protracted impact of the COVID-19 pandemic through

loss of jobs and the collapse of social safety nets, which left many Americans—particularly those from minoritized backgrounds—unprotected (Moffitt & Ziliak, 2020).

While the data point to various health challenges that the Black community of Alaska experiences, there are also important protective factors such as high levels of health insurance coverage, self-efficacy, and community. In addition, this assessment was initiated and led by a Black-led grassroots organization committed to addressing the health challenges in the Black community. Acknowledging strength and resilience alongside disease and ill health is therefore a central aspect of the Black Alaska experience of health (Taylor & Chatters, 1988).

IMPLICATIONS FOR SOCIAL WORK IN HEALTH

This assessment contains important implications for social workers. First, it further confirms that despite the growing federal and local attention to health disparities, there is strong evidence of their persistence particularly as exposed by the COVID-19 pandemic (Bowen & Walton, 2015). Social workers should continue to use research-based approaches to illuminate health issues among Black people and other minoritized communities.

It is also essential for social workers to advocate for policies that broadly affect the social determinants of health of Black people. For example, policies that look at the Black experience with the criminal justice system, in rural and remote communities, and in education, housing, employment, and other social institutions.

At the same time, social workers should balance a health-affirming, nonpathologizing view with honest engagement with the health issues that the Black community experiences. This is important for reducing the disproportionate burden of illness among Black people and will help to build trust with members of the Black community.

Social workers must also continue to build community-based partnerships to address health issues and related disparities in underrepresented communities. This is essential for closing barriers to accessing care and for building trusting relationships between the health providers and the communities they serve.

Last, by providing the state of Alaska its first reference point for information and data on the health of Black Alaskans, the assessment has set the stage for continued advocacy, education, and investment in the health of Black Alaskans. It has also proven the capacity of a small, grassroots, Black-led organization to meaningfully effect change and galvanize state efforts to respond to the health needs of an underserved population. We believe that this impetus will continue to resonate throughout the healthcare system, and especially in social work, to collect health information on Black Alaskans and deliberately seek to close the gaps in healthcare access for Black Alaskans.

LIMITATIONS

This article presents findings from the quantitative survey of Black Alaskans. As such, we are unable to compare the health status of Black Alaskans with other racial and ethnic groups. A comparative analysis of health status data is presented separately. **HSW**

REFERENCES

American Public Health Association. (2021). *Advancing racial equity.* https://www.apha.org/-/media/Files/PDF/topics/racism/Racism_Declarations_Analysis.ashx

Awad, G. H., Abuelezam, N. N., Ajrouch, K. J., & Stiffler, M. J. (2022). Lack of Arab or Middle Eastern and North African health data undermines assessment of health disparities. *American Journal of Public Health, 112,* 209–212. https://doi.org/10.2105/AJPH.2021.306590

Balls-Berry, J. E., & Acosta-Pérez, E. (2017). The use of community engaged research principles to improve health: Community academic partnerships for research. *Puerto Rico Health Sciences Journal, 36,* 84–85.

Barnidge, E. K., Baker, E. A., Schootman, M., Motton, F., Sawicki, M., & Rose, F. (2015). The effect of education plus access on perceived fruit and vegetable consumption in a rural African American community intervention. *Health Education Research, 30,* 773–785. https://doi.org/10.1093/her/cyv041

Belgrave, F., Abrams, J., Smalley, K., & Warren C. (2021). African American health equity. In K. B. Smalley, J. C. Warren, & M. I. Fernández (Eds.), *Health equity: A solutions-focused approach.* Springer.

Bowen, E. A., & Walton, Q. L. (2015). Disparities and the social determinants of mental health and addictions: Opportunities for a multifaceted social work response. *Health & Social Work, 40,* e59–e65. https://doi.org/10.1093/hsw/hlv034

Buckingham, S. L., Mbise, A., Chen, T., Kuhn, S., Gat, N., & Sytniak, S., (2022). *Conducting multilingual qualitative research online on immigrant integration and inclusion* [Case]. SAGE. https://dx.doi.org/10.4135/9781529601770

García-Rivera, E. J., Pacheco, P., Colón, M., Mays, M. H., Rivera, M., Munet-Díaz, V., González, M. D. R., Rodríguez, M., Rodríguez, R., & Morales, A. (2017). Building bridges to address health disparities in Puerto Rico: The "Salud para Piñones" Project. *Puerto Rico Health Sciences Journal, 36,* 92–100.

Golden, S. H. (2020, April 20). *Coronavirus in African Americans and other people of color.* Johns Hopkins Medicine. https://www.hopkinsmedicine.org/health/conditions-and-diseases/coronavirus/covid19-racial-disparities

Grant, C. G., Ramos, R., Davis, J. L., & Green, B. L. (2015). Community health needs assessment: A pathway to the future and a vision for leaders. *Health Care Manager, 34,* 147–156. https://doi.org/10.1097/HCM.0000000000000057

Hartman, I. C. (2021). *Black history in the last frontier.* National Park Service; University of Alaska Anchorage. https://www.nps.gov/articles/upload/BLACK-History-in-the-Last-Frontier_Reader_Compressed.pdf

Israel, B. A., Coombe, C. M., Cheezum, R. R., Schulz, A. J., McGranaghan, R. J., Lichtenstein, R., Reyes, A. G., Clement, J., & Burris, A. (2010). Community-based participatory research: A capacity-building approach for policy advocacy aimed at eliminating health disparities. *American Journal of Public Health, 100,* 2094–2102. https://doi.org/10.2105/AJPH.2009.170506

Moffitt, R., & Ziliak, J. (2020). *COVID-19 and the U.S. safety net* (NBER Working Paper No. 27911). https://www.nber.org/system/files/working_papers/w27911/w27911.pdf

Office of Disease Prevention and Health Promotion. (n.d.). *Health equity in Healthy People 2030.* U.S. Department of Health and Human Services. https://health.gov/healthypeople/priority-areas/health-equity-healthy-people-2030

Payán, D. D., Lewis, L. B., Illum, J., Hawkins, B., & Sloane, D. C. (2022). United for health to improve urban food environments across five underserved communities: A cross-sector coalition approach. *BMC Public Health, 22,* Article 888. https://doi.org/10.1186/s12889-022-13245-2

Shimizu, R., Mbise, A., Garcia, G., Brown, C., Leigh, J., Growden, C. H., Hourigan, H., & Bemben, T. A. (2022, November 6–9). *Black Alaskan health status report: Examining racial differences in morbidity.* American Public Health Association Conference, Boston, MA, United States.

Smalley, K. B., Warren, J. C., & Fernández, M. I. (2021). Health equity: Overview, history, and key concepts. In K. B. Smalley, J. C. Warren, & M. I. Fernández (Eds.). *Health equity: A solutions-focused approach* (pp. 3–12). Springer.

Taylor, R. J., & Chatters, L. M. (1988). Church members as a source of informal social support. *Review of Religious Research, 30,* 193–203. https://doi.org/10.2307/3511355

U.S. Census Bureau. (n.d.). *QuickFacts: Alaska.* Retrieved November 26, 2022, from https://www.census.gov/quickfacts/fact/table/AK/RHI225222

U.S. Department of Health and Human Services. (2011). *Principles of community engagement* (2nd ed.). NIH Publications. https://www.atsdr.cdc.gov/communityengagement/pdf/PCE_Report_508_FINAL.pdf

Villablanca, A. C., Warford, C., & Wheeler, K. (2016). Inflammation and cardiometabolic risk in African American women is reduced by a pilot community-based educational intervention. *Journal of Women's Health, 25,* 188–199. https://doi.org/10.1089/jwh.2014.5109

Ward, M., Schulz, A. J., Israel, B. A., Rice, K., Martenies, S. E., & Markarian, E. (2018). A conceptual framework for evaluating health equity promotion within community-based participatory research partnerships.

Evaluation and Program Planning, 70, 25–34. https://doi.org/10.1016/j.evalprogplan.2018.04.014

Amana Mbise, PhD, is assistant professor, School of Social Work, University of Alaska Anchorage, 3211 Providence Drive, PSB 224B, Anchorage, AK 99508, USA; email: ambise@alaska.edu. **Celeste Hodge-Growden** is president/CEO, Alaska Black Caucus, Anchorage, AK, USA. **Thea Bemben,** is principal and cofounder, Agnew::Beck Consulting, Inc., Anchorage, AK, USA. **Rei Shimizu, PhD,** is assistant professor, School of Social Work, University of Alaska Anchorage, Anchorage, AK, USA. This project was delivered through a partnership with the University of Alaska Anchorage School of Social Work and the Alaska Black Caucus through a grant by the Municipality of Anchorage, Anchorage Health Department [Award G14536]. The views expressed here are solely those of the authors.

Original manuscript received March 2, 2023
Final revision received June 15, 2023
Editorial decision July 24, 2023
Accepted July 24, 2023
Advance Access Publication March 15, 2024

READERS: WRITE TO US!

Submit your reactions to and comments about an article published in *Health & Social Work* or a contemporary issue in the field. Send your letter (three double-spaced pages or fewer) as a Word document through the online portal at http://hsw.msubmit.net (initial, one-time registration is required).

IDENTIFYING MORAL PANIC

THE DISCOURSE OF FEAR IN SOCIAL POLICY

MICHAEL H. EVERSMAN

Using the sociological framework of moral panic—periods of exaggerated public fear triggered by high-profile incidents linked to feared social groups—Eversman illuminates historic and contemporary moral panic episodes to show how political discourse and stereotyping lead to policymaking and enforcement that maintain social inequalities. Those most affected by these harsh and reactionary policies tend to be vulnerable populations known as "folk devils"—young people, public assistance recipients, immigrants, LGBTQ individuals, those with mental illness, and illicit drug users—groups that have long served as feared targets of moral condemnation.

As a core social policy text, this book emphasizes the social justice mission of professional social work and the need to stay vigilant amid structural inequalities rooted in labeling and otherism, allowing readers to recognize the patterns of moral panic discourse as constructed in various societal arenas, identify important media functions, and think critically about social problems.

**ISBN: 978-0-87101-576-1. 2022.
Item #5761. 208 pages.
1-800-227-3590 • www.naswpress.org**

NASW PRESS

NASW
National Association of Social Workers
APIMT22

Interpersonal VIOLENCE
The Social Work Response
TRICIA B. BENT-GOODLEY, EDITOR

Interpersonal violence, including intimate partner violence (IPV), impacts all communities regardless of race and ethnicity, sexual orientation, age, disability, religion, class, or national origin. Yet, some people—such as those with disabilities, those who identify as LGBTQ, and women of color—are disproportionately impacted. *Interpersonal Violence: The Social Work Response* proposes that it is essential for social workers to understand the evolving and persistent landscape of interpersonal violence, including concurrent victimization, overlapping patterns, and intersections. The book encourages a three-pronged approach, one that is trauma informed, culturally responsive, and survivor centered. Covering a wide range of environments in which social workers work with IPV, contributors offer a variety of innovative methods for working with victims, including constructed agency, antioppressive frameworks, community engagement, and work with abusive persons.

NASW PRESS

ISBN: 978-0-87101-586-0 (pbk). 2023.
Item #5860. 284 pages.
1-800-227-3590 www.naswpress.org

National Association of Social Workers

APIVT23

Examining the Role of Self-Harm in the Relationship between Emergency Department Service Utilization and Trauma-Induced Homelessness among Homeless Individuals in Texas

Sumaita Choudhury, Sharon Lee Choi, Yehyang Lee, and Stacey Stevens Manser

Homelessness is a complex public health problem in the United States. Current or ongoing history of trauma among individuals adds to the complexity and challenges of homelessness. Our study assessed the moderating role of self-harm in the association between emergency department (ED) service utilization and trauma-induced homelessness (TIH) among adults in Texas. Homeless adults ($N = 282$) who completed their baseline Vulnerability Index Service Prioritization Decision Assistance Prescreen Tool survey between February 2021 and February 2022 at a Local Mental Health Authority in Texas were selected. The outcome variable, TIH, was assessed by current period of homelessness due to experiencing trauma or abuse. The main independent variable was ED utilization, while self-harm in the past year was assessed as the moderating variable. A multivariate logistic regression with a moderation analysis was conducted while adjusting for the covariates. Individuals who utilized ED services and engaged in self-harm and risky behaviors had greater odds of experiencing current period of TIH. Male respondents were less likely to experience TIH. Finally, engaging in self-harm significantly moderated the association between ED service use and TIH. This study may help inform efforts to develop tailored interventions and promote resilience-based approaches to improve health outcomes among individuals experiencing homelessness due to TIH.

KEY WORDS: *emergency department service utilization; homelessness; self-harm; trauma*

omelessness is a complex public health problem in the United States, contributing to adverse mental and physical health outcomes (Mackelprang et al., 2014; Salhi et al., 2018). The U.S. Department of Housing and Urban Development (HUD) has outlined four categories of homelessness, which include "literally homeless" (i.e., family or individual without a stable or regular residence for sleeping purposes), "imminent risk of homelessness" (i.e., family or individual who are at a higher risk of losing their primary form of living), "homeless under other federal statuses" (i.e., young adults under the age of 25 who do not qualify under federal statuses as homeless individuals), and "fleeing/attempting to flee domestic violence" (i.e., family or individual who is trying to escape a violent household; HUD, 2019). The number of individuals experiencing homelessness has been on the rise in the United States since 2017 (National Alliance to End Homelessness, 2023). A recent public health report revealed that approximately 580,000 individuals were experiencing homelessness at the start of the pandemic, of whom 225,000 were reported unsheltered (Henry et al., 2021; Mosites et al., 2022).

Trauma-induced homelessness (TIH), stemming from a complex synergy of adverse or traumatic life experiences (e.g., domestic violence, assault), poses a critical challenge in understanding and addressing homelessness-related issues. Previous research has indicated that domestic violence is one of the leading causes of experiencing homelessness, especially among women with children in the United States (Baker et al., 2010). In addition, the National Network to End Domestic Violence (2016) reported that during a single day in 2015, approximately 31,500 individuals with children sought refuge in transitional housing and emergency shelters due to domestic violence; however, most of those shelter requests were unfulfilled due to a lack of resources from homeless service programs. Although there are existing national estimates of individuals experiencing homelessness, it should be noted that homelessness is severely underreported in Texas, and no overall statistical number or percentage represents the accurate number of individuals experiencing homelessness in recent years, particularly for TIH. Thus, better strategies are needed to gather more accurate data, especially for individuals experiencing current period of TIH in Texas.

Homelessness is a significant risk factor for high emergency department (ED) service utilization (Amato et al., 2019; Hwang et al., 2013; Lebrun-Harris et al., 2013; Moulin et al., 2018). Individuals experiencing homelessness are more likely to use ED services than individuals with stable housing (Abramson et al., 2021). In addition, homeless individuals are at heightened risk of returning to the ED within a month of their prior visit (Amato et al., 2019). Increased ED use among homeless populations can be due to various factors, including risky behaviors (e.g., substance abuse, unprotected sex), violence-related injuries, mental illness, and lack of primary or preventive care (Amato et al., 2019). Additionally, individuals' current period of homelessness due to experiencing violence such as physical assault, abuse, psychological trauma, or domestic violence has been shown to lead to catastrophic situations such as increased ED service use and engaging in self-harm (Miller et al., 2020; Moore et al., 2007).

Previous research has predominantly examined the association between self-harm and ED service utilization within homeless populations (Clements et al., 2022); domestic violence–related homelessness and its relationship with higher ED service utilization (Narendorf, 2017; Riley et al., 2020); and connections between domestic abuse, TIH, and self-mutilating behavior among homeless youths (Tyler et al., 2003). Although most of these studies have established a significant relationship between these variables, none explored the interaction between TIH, self-harm, and ED service utilization within the homeless population, specifically how the relationship between ED service use and TIH might differ based on self-harm behavior. To address these gaps, this study will evaluate the moderating role of self-harm in the association between ED service utilization and TIH among homeless individuals in Texas. Findings from this study can help inform future interventions to improve access to mental health and primary care services, provide long-term housing stability, and additional resources for individuals experiencing current TIH.

METHOD
Data Source and Study Population
We conducted a secondary data analysis utilizing data collected from February 2021 to February 2022 through the Vulnerability Index Service Prioritization Decision Assistance Tool (VI-SPDAT). The dataset was collected by a Local Mental Health Authority (LMHA) organization located in Texas focusing on adults experiencing homelessness. The VI-SPDAT is a prescreening tool that homeless or clinical service providers administer during the coordinated entry process to evaluate the health and social necessities among individuals and families experiencing homelessness and assist them in finding suitable housing and supportive interventions (Greater Richmond Continuum of Care, n.d.). The LMHA is part of the Healthy Community Collaborative, a state-funded program managed by the Texas Health and Human Services Commission to increase access to housing services among individuals experiencing homelessness who have severe mental illnesses or co-occurring substance use disorders. This study includes a sample of 282 homeless adults aged 21 to 75 years who completed their baseline VI-SPDAT during their intake process.

VI-SPDAT Measures
The dependent variable was current period of homelessness due to experiencing trauma or abuse or TIH. TIH was assessed by a single self-reported item: "Has your current period of homelessness been caused by an experience of emotional, physical, psychological, sexual, or other type of abuse, or by any other trauma you have experienced?" Response options were yes or no.

Independent variables included ED service utilization, self-harm behavior, and engaging in risky behaviors.

ED Service Utilization. The primary independent continuous variable of the study was self-reported ED service utilization, assessed by one item: "How many times have you received healthcare at an emergency department/room?"

with response options ranging from "0 times" to "greater than 10 times."

Self-Harm Behavior. Past-year self-harm or threatening to inflict harm to others was assessed by a single item: "Have you threatened to or tried to harm yourself or anyone else in the last year?" Response options were "yes" or "no."

Engaging in Risky Behaviors. Self-reported risky behaviors were evaluated by a single item: "Do you ever do things that may be considered to be risky, like exchange sex for money, run drugs for someone, have unprotected sex with someone you don't know, share a needle, or anything like that?" Response options were "yes" or "no."

Covariates

Sociodemographic variables that were controlled for in this study were based on previous evidence (Amato et al., 2019; Miller et al., 2020; Moore et al., 2007; Tyler et al., 2003). Sociodemographic variables included age (21 to 75 years), gender (female or male), race (recoded into three categories: White, Black or African American, or other), ethnicity (non-Hispanic/non-Latino or Hispanic/Latino), and marital status (recoded into three categories: single, married, or divorced/widowed/separated).

Statistical Analyses

All statistical analyses were conducted using STATA (Version 17.0). Descriptive statistical analyses, including frequency and percentage distributions, were reported for categorical variables. Means and standard deviations were reported for the continuous variables. We conducted bivariate analyses using Pearson chi-square (χ^2) tests and independent t tests to examine the differences among ED service utilization, engaging in risky behaviors, self-harm, and the covariate variables (age, gender, race, ethnicity, and marital status) between homeless adults whose current period of homelessness was not related to TIH versus homeless adults who were currently experiencing TIH. Multivariable logistic regression was conducted with estimated adjusted odds ratios (a*OR*s) to examine the association between ED service utilization and TIH while adjusting for risky behaviors, self-harm, and all covariates. Finally, moderation analysis was performed to examine whether the effects of ED service utilization on TIH vary by self-harm while adjusting for risky behaviors and all covariates.

RESULTS
Sample Characteristics and Bivariate Analysis

Our study sample includes 282 homeless adults who completed their baseline VI-SPDAT assessments. The mean age of our study population was 50 years, and they were predominantly male (65 percent), White (58 percent), non-Hispanic/non-Latino (82 percent), and single (61 percent). Overall, individuals used ED service an average of three times, and approximately 55 percent of the sample reported engagement in risky behaviors and self-harm. Table 1 also displays the independent bivariate associations between each independent variable and TIH. TIH significantly varied by gender, as female respondents exhibited a notably higher likelihood of TIH than male respondents (91.8 percent vs. 79.9 percent; $p < .01$). Individuals who engaged in risky behaviors reported a higher rate of TIH than those who did not (95.5 percent vs. 70.3 percent; $p < .001$). Moreover, individuals who reported self-harm or threatened to inflict harm to others reported higher odds of TIH than those who did not engage in self-harm (96.8 percent vs. 68.3 percent; $p < .001$). Finally, individuals who were experiencing current period of TIH used an average of 3.50 (±3.32) ED services, which was significantly higher compared with the average ED service utilization (1.49 [±2.24]) among individuals who were not experiencing TIH ($p < .001$). No other significant differences were found for age, race, ethnicity, and marital status.

Multivariate Analysis

The logistic regression results are presented in Table 2. Results showed that compared with female respondents, male respondents were less likely to experience TIH (a*OR* = 0.32; 95% CI [0.12, 0.82]; $p < .05$). Our findings also demonstrated a significant association between ED service utilization and TIH (a*OR* =1.26; 95% CI [1.04, 1.51]; $p < .05$). Compared with individuals who did not engage in risky behaviors, individuals who did engage in risky behaviors reported higher odds of experiencing TIH (a*OR* = 3.57; 95% CI [1.38, 9.23]; $p < .01$). Finally, individuals who engaged in self-harm behavior or threatened to inflict harm to others were significantly more likely to suffer from TIH (a*OR* = 7.25; 95% CI [2.52, 20.88]; $p < .001$).

Table 1: Descriptive Statistics and Bivariate Analyses of Characteristics by Current Period TIH (*N* = 282)

Variable	Total *n*	Total (%)	No (*n* = 45) *n*	No (*n* = 45) (%)	Yes (*n* = 237) *n*	Yes (*n* = 237) (%)	*p* value
Gender							<.01[b]
Female	98	(34.75)	8	(8.16)	90	(91.84)	
Male	184	(65.25)	37	(20.11)	147	(79.89)	
Race							.751[b]
Black or African American	103	(36.52)	18	(17.48)	85	(85.52)	
White	164	(58.16)	24	(14.63)	140	(85.37)	
Other	15	(5.32)	3	(20.00)	12	(80.00)	
Ethnicity							.901[b]
Hispanic/Latino	52	(18.44)	8	(15.38)	44	(84.62)	
Non–Hispanic/non–Latino	230	(81.56)	37	(16.09)	193	(83.91)	
Marital status							.285[b]
Married	18	(6.38)	3	(16.67)	15	(83.33)	
Single	173	(61.35)	32	(18.50)	141	(81.50)	
Divorced/separated/widowed	91	(32.37)	10	(10.99)	81	(89.01)	
Risky behaviors							<.001[b]
No	128	(45.39)	38	(29.69)	90	(70.31)	
Yes	154	(54.61)	7	(4.55)	147	(95.45)	
Self-harm							<.001[b]
No	126	(44.68)	40	(31.75)	86	(68.25)	
Yes	156	(55.32)	5	(3.21)	151	(96.79)	
	M	*(SD)*	*M*	*(SD)*	*M*	*(SD)*	
Age (years)	50.19	(10.99)	52.22	12.31	49.81	10.70	.178[a]
ED utilization	3.18	(3.25)	1.49	2.24	3.50	3.32	<.001[a]

Notes: TIH = trauma-induced homelessness; ED = emergency department.
[a]Independent *t* test.
[b]Chi-squared test.

Moderation Analysis

Figure 1 exhibits the moderation analysis using a marginsplot on whether self-harm behavior moderates the relationship between ED service utilization and TIH while adjusting for risky behaviors and all covariates. Results showed that engaging in self-harm significantly moderated the relationship between ED service utilization and TIH ($p < .05$). Individuals who used ED services 10 or more times and engaged in self-harm behavior had the highest likelihood of experiencing TIH compared with those who used ED services at least three times.

DISCUSSION

Our study examined whether the association between ED service utilization and TIH varies by engaging in self-harm behavior among a group of homeless adults in Texas. Results indicated that engaging in self-harm significantly moderated the association between ED utilization and TIH. Compared with existing studies that have primarily assessed the association between self-harm, domestic violence, ED service utilization, and homelessness (Clements et al., 2022; Narendorf, 2017; Riley et al., 2020; Tyler et al., 2003), our study provides further insights into the interplay between ED service utilization, self-harm, and TIH, demonstrating how the impact of ED service utilization on TIH varied significantly by self-harm behavior.

Our study also found a significant association between engaging in risky behaviors (e.g., exchange sex for money, run drugs for someone) and TIH. These findings add to the previous literature that reported how experiencing abuse, severe mental

Table 2: Multivariable Logistic Regression of Current Period of TIH and Its Association with ED Service Utilization, Risky Behaviors, Self-Harm, and Covariates

Variable	aOR	95% CI
Age	0.99	[0.96, 1.03]
Gender (ref.: female)		
Male	0.32*	[0.12, 0.82]
Race (ref.: Black or African American)		
White	0.82	[0.35, 1.94]
Other	0.74	[0.13, 4.40]
Ethnicity (ref.: Hispanic/Latino)		
Non-Hispanic/non-Latino	1.33	[0.44, 4.05]
Marital status (ref.: married)		
Single	0.67	[0.14, 3.17]
Divorced/separated/widowed	0.81	[0.15, 4.53]
ED service utilization	1.26*	[1.04, 1.51]
Risky behaviors (ref.: no)		
Yes	3.57**	[1.38, 9.23]
Self-harm (ref.: no)		
Yes	7.25***	[2.52, 20.88]

Notes: TIH = trauma-induced homelessness; ED = emergency department; aOR = adjusted odds ratio; CI = confidence interval; ref. = reference group.
*$p < .05$. **$p < .01$. ***$p < .001$.

health disorders, engaging in risky behaviors, and self-harm have been associated with homelessness (O'Brien Gewirtz et al., 2020; Pluck et al., 2013; Tyler et al., 2010). Previous studies have consistently demonstrated that over 50 percent of homeless individuals have visited the ED at least once, a proportion significantly higher than the national average (Bharel et al., 2013; Kushel et al., 2001; Kushel et al., 2002; Lin et al., 2015). Notably, our study findings indicate that the rates of ED visits are even higher (three or more times), especially among homeless individuals with a history of abuse.

Even though previous studies have found significant associations between sociodemographic factors (e.g., age, gender, race/ethnicity, income, marital status, and health insurance status) and homelessness (Byrne et al., 2016; National Alliance to End Homelessness, 2023; Nilsson et al., 2019), our study found that female respondents were at higher risks of experiencing TIH. However, it should be noted that previous literature has predominantly focused on the correlation between these sociodemographic factors and homelessness in a broader context. In contrast, our study assessed these factors among adults experiencing TIH.

Figure 1: Moderation by Engaging in Self-Harm Behavior

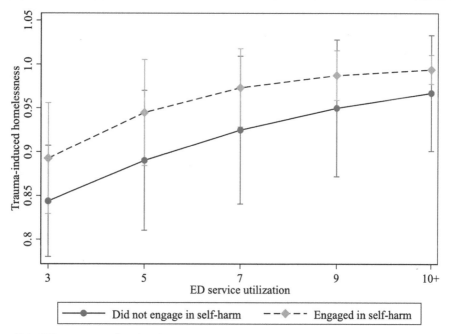

Note: ED = emergency department.

Furthermore, Unlike previous studies that have primarily focused on adolescents and young adults when evaluating the relationship between self-harm and homelessness, our study sample included homeless adults with a broader age group ($M = 50$ years; range: 21 to 75) and uncovered both risky behaviors (e.g., having unprotected sex) and self-harm to be significantly associated with TIH (Barnes et al., 2018; Cutuli et al., 2020; Heerde et al., 2020).

Limitations

While our findings provide a further understanding of the interplay between TIH, ED service utilization, and the consequences of self-harm among homeless adults in Texas, this study is not without limitations. As we used a cross-sectional study design, temporality cannot be established. Thus, no temporal inferences can be made regarding the moderating effect of self-harm on the association between ED service utilization and the current period of TIH. Our study sample also limits the generalizability of our findings, as the participants were homeless adults with serious mental health or co-occurring substance use disorders and a history of trauma, self-harm, and risky behaviors seeking homelessness services in Texas. In addition, this study utilized items from the VI-SPDAT, which has received criticism for its inconsistent reliability and validity, which can create further issues in measuring homelessness-related outcomes (Brown et al., 2018) across different populations and timeframes (Brown et al., 2018; Currie et al., 2021). For example, the VI-SPDAT item that was used to assess the outcome variable for this study, which is whether any type of trauma has caused the current period of TIH, is definitionally and operationally multifaceted and can lead to difficulties in distinguishing which type of trauma (i.e., psychological, sexual, emotional, physical, or other type of abuse) caused the current period of TIH. Furthermore, the single VI-SPDAT item related to TIH leads to additional questions regarding the periods and frequencies of trauma individuals have experienced.

The moderating variable in this study (self-harm) was also assessed by a single complex item that asks the individual whether, in the past year, they have harmed themselves or threatened to inflict harm to others, making it hard to discern what number of individuals had ideation of self-harm, conducted self-harm, imposed harm to others, or experienced a combination thereof. Additionally, the self-harm item does not ascertain the timing of self-harm incidents among individuals, mainly whether it occurred before homelessness, during the period of homelessness, or concurrently. Furthermore, the item that assessed engagement in other types of risky behaviors also asked about various behaviors (e.g., having unprotected sex, prostitution, substance abuse), making it difficult to understand the frequencies, periods of engaging in risky behaviors, and burdens of each type of risky behavior among individuals experiencing homelessness. Thus, it is imperative to revisit and reassess these VI-SPDAT items and develop newer items pertaining to these complex constructs to understand the nuances of these items and report accurate results.

This study has several potential biases due to utilizing the VI-SPDAT as it relies on self-reported data, which can lead to social desirability or recall bias. Another potential bias in this study is interviewer bias. As homeless service providers collected the VI-SPDAT items at the LMHA, the interaction between the providers and the homeless adults may have led to over- or underrepresentation in the data. Thus, future studies should conduct interviews with service providers to assess how these questions are answered and what steps should be taken to improve the VI-SPDAT. Finally, our study sample includes only the baseline VI-SPDAT data that may involve at-risk acute-stage individuals trying to get placed in a homeless shelter, which could explain why the data were heavily skewed toward high ED utilization, higher engagement in risky behaviors, and more self-harm. Therefore, in the future, we plan to conduct longitudinal studies to assess the effectiveness of how the homeless service programs aided its participants with their homelessness-related challenges.

Conclusion

Coping with complex trauma and self-harm can be highly challenging, especially among homeless populations. It is also essential to recognize that engaging in self-harm is not always an intentional behavior, and individuals should not be shamed as such behaviors often arise as negative coping mechanisms to deal with the effects of their ongoing or previous traumatic experiences (Sheehy et al., 2019). Findings from this study may help inform efforts to develop strategic interventions and promote resilience-based approaches among individuals experiencing TIH and clinical service providers to help reduce ED use, decrease the rates of self-harm and risky behaviors, and improve overall physical and mental health outcomes and quality of life. HSW

REFERENCES

Abramson, T. M., Sanko, S., & Eckstein, M. (2021). Emergency medical services utilization by homeless patients. *Prehospital Emergency Care, 25*, 333–340. https://doi.org/10.1080/10903127.2020.1777234

Amato, S., Nobay, F., Amato, D. P., Abar, B., & Adler, D. (2019). Sick and unsheltered: Homelessness as a major risk factor for emergency care utilization. *American Journal of Emergency Medicine, 37*, 415–420. https://doi.org/10.1016/j.ajem.2018.06.001

Baker, C. K., Billhardt, K. A., Warren, J., Rollins, C., & Glass, N. E. (2010). Domestic violence, housing instability, and homelessness: A review of housing policies and program practices for meeting the needs of survivors. *Aggression and Violent Behavior, 15*, 430–439. https://doi.org/10.1016/j.avb.2010.07.005

Barnes, A. J., Gilbertson, J., & Chatterjee, D. (2018). Emotional health among youth experiencing family homelessness. *Pediatrics, 141*, Article e20171767. https://doi.org/10.1542/peds.2017-1767

Bharel, M., Lin, W.-C., Zhang, J., O'Connell, E., Taube, R., & Clark, R. E. (2013). Health care utilization patterns of homeless individuals in Boston: Preparing for Medicaid expansion under the Affordable Care Act. *American Journal of Public Health, 103*, S311–S317. https://doi.org/10.2105/AJPH.2013.301421

Brown, M., Cummings, C., Lyons, J., Carrión, A., & Watson, D. P. (2018). Reliability and validity of the Vulnerability Index-Service Prioritization Decision Assistance Tool (VI-SPDAT) in real-world implementation. *Journal of Social Distress and Homelessness, 27*, 110–117. https://doi.org/10.1080/10530789.2018.1482991

Byrne, T., Treglia, D., Culhane, D. P., Kuhn, J., & Kane, V. (2016). Predictors of homelessness among families and single adults after exit from homelessness prevention and rapid re-housing programs: Evidence from the Department of Veterans Affairs Supportive Services for Veteran Families Program. *Housing Policy Debate, 26*, 252–275. https://doi.org/10.1080/10511482.2015.1060249

Clements, C., Farooq, B., Hawton, K., Geulayov, G., Casey, D., Waters, K., Ness, J., Patel, A., Townsend, E., Appleby, L., & Kapur, N. (2022). Self-harm in people experiencing homelessness: Investigation of incidence, characteristics and outcomes using data from the Multicentre Study of Self-Harm in England. *BJPsych Open, 8*, Article e74. https://doi.org/10.1192/bjo.2022.30

Currie, J., Grech, E., Longbottom, E., Yee, J., Hastings, R., Aitkenhead, A., Cason, A., & Obrecht, K. (2021). Scoping review of the characteristics assessed by vulnerability indices applied to people experiencing homelessness. *PLOS ONE, 16*, Article e0254100. https://doi.org/10.1371/journal.pone.0254100

Cutuli, J. J., Treglia, D., & Herbers, J. E. (2020). Adolescent homelessness and associated features: Prevalence and risk across eight states. *Child Psychiatry & Human Development, 51*, 48–58. https://doi.org/10.1007/s10578-019-00909-1

Greater Richmond Continuum of Care. (n.d.). *VI-SPDAT*. Retrieved August 22, 2022, from https://www.endhomelessnessrva.org/vi-spdat

Heerde, J. A., Bailey, J. A., Toumbourou, J. W., Rowland, B., & Catalano, R. F. (2020). Prevalence of homelessness and co-occurring problems: A comparison of young adults in Victoria, Australia and Washington State, United States. *Children and Youth Services Review, 109*, Article 104692. https://doi.org/10.1016/j.childyouth.2019.104692

Henry, M., de Sousa, T., Roddey, C., Gayen, S., & Bednar, T. J. (2021). *The 2020 annual homeless assessment report (AHAR) to Congress*. U.S. Department of Housing and Urban Development. https://www.huduser.gov/portal/sites/default/files/pdf/2020-ahar-part-1.pdf

Hwang, S. W., Chambers, C., Chiu, S., Katic, M., Kiss, A., Redelmeier, D. A., & Levinson, W. (2013). A comprehensive assessment of health care utilization among homeless adults under a system of universal health insurance. *American Journal of Public Health, 103*, S294–S301. https://doi.org/10.2105/AJPH.2013.301369

Kushel, M. B., Perry, S., Bangsberg, D., Clark, R., & Moss, A. R. (2002). Emergency department use among the homeless and marginally housed: Results from a community-based study. *American Journal of Public Health, 92*, 778–784. https://doi.org/10.2105/AJPH.92.5.778

Kushel, M. B., Vittinghoff, E., & Haas, J. S. (2001). Factors associated with the health care utilization of homeless persons. *JAMA, 285*, 200–206. https://doi.org/10.1001/jama.285.2.200

Lebrun-Harris, L. A., Baggett, T. P., Jenkins, D. M., Sripipatana, A., Sharma, R., Hayashi, A. S., Daly, C. A., & Ngo-Metzger, Q. (2013). Health status and health care experiences among homeless patients in federally supported health centers: Findings from the 2009 Patient Survey. *Health Services Research, 48*, 992–1017. https://doi.org/10.1111/1475-6773.12009

Lin, W.-C., Bharel, M., Zhang, J., O'Connell, E., & Clark, R. E. (2015). Frequent emergency department visits and hospitalizations among homeless people with Medicaid: Implications for Medicaid expansion. *American Journal of Public Health, 105*, S716–S722. https://doi.org/10.2105/AJPH.2015.302693

Mackelprang, J. L., Klest, B., Najmabadi, S. J., Valley-Gray, S., Gonzalez, E. A., & Cash, R. E. (2014). Betrayal trauma among homeless adults: Associations with revictimization, psychological well-being, and health. *Journal of Interpersonal Violence, 29*, 1028–1049. https://doi.org/10.1177/0886260513506060

Miller, J.-P., O'Reilly, G. M., Mackelprang, J. L., & Mitra, B. (2020). Trauma in adults experiencing homelessness. *Injury, 51*, 897–905. https://doi.org/10.1016/j.injury.2020.02.086

Moore, G., Gerdtz, M., & Manias, E. (2007). Homelessness, health status and emergency department use: An integrated review of the literature. *Australasian Emergency Nursing Journal, 10*, 178–185. https://doi.org/10.1016/j.aenj.2007.07.003

Mosites, E., Harrison, B., Montgomery, M. P., Meehan, A. A., Leopold, J., Barranco, L., Schwerzler, L., Carmichael, A. E., Clarke, K. E. N., & Butler, J. C. (2022). Public health lessons learned in responding to COVID-19 among people experiencing homelessness in the United States. *Public Health Reports, 137*, 625–629. https://doi.org/10.1177/00333549221083643

Moulin, A., Evans, E. J., Xing, G., & Melnikow, J. (2018). Substance use, homelessness, mental illness and Medicaid coverage: A set-up for high emergency department utilization. *Western Journal of Emergency Medicine, 19*, 902–906. https://doi.org/10.5811/westjem.2018.9.38954

Narendorf, S. C. (2017). Intersection of homelessness and mental health: A mixed methods study of young adults who accessed psychiatric emergency services. *Children and Youth Services Review, 81,* 54–62. https://doi.org/10.1016/j.childyouth.2017.07.024

National Alliance to End Homelessness. (2023). *State of homelessness: 2023 edition.* https://endhomelessness.org/homelessness-in-america/homelessness-statistics/state-of-homelessness/

National Network to End Domestic Violence. (2016). *Domestic violence counts 2015: A 24-hour census of domestic violence shelters and services.* https://www.acf.hhs.gov/ofvps/fact-sheet/domestic-violence-and-homelessness-statistics-2016

Nilsson, S. F., Nordentoft, M., & Hjorthøj, C. (2019). Individual-level predictors for becoming homeless and exiting homelessness: A systematic review and meta-analysis. *Journal of Urban Health, 96,* 741–750. https://doi.org/10.1007/s11524-019-00377-x

O'Brien Gewirtz, J. R., Edinburgh, L. D., Barnes, A. J., & McRee, A.-L. (2020). Mental health outcomes among homeless, runaway, and stably housed youth. *Pediatrics, 145,* Article e20192674. https://doi.org/10.1542/peds.2019-2674

Pluck, G., Lee, K.-H., & Parks, R. W. (2013). Self-harm and homeless adults. *Journal of Crisis Intervention and Suicide Prevention, 34,* 363–366. https://doi.org/10.1027/0227-5910/a000202

Riley, E. D., Vittinghoff, E., Kagawa, R. M. C., Raven, M. C., Eagen, K. V., Cohee, A., Dilworth, S. E., & Shumway, M. (2020). Violence and emergency department use among community-recruited women who experience homelessness and housing instability. *Journal of Urban Health, 97,* 78–87. https://doi.org/10.1007/s11524-019-00404-x

Salhi, B. A., White, M. H., Pitts, S. R., & Wright, D. W. (2018). Homelessness and emergency medicine: A review of the literature. *Academic Emergency Medicine, 25,* 577–593. https://doi.org/10.1111/acem.13358

Sheehy, K., Noureen, A., Khaliq, A., Dhingra, K., Husain, N., Pontin, E. E., Cawley, R., & Taylor, P. J. (2019). An examination of the relationship between shame, guilt and self-harm: A systematic review and meta-analysis. *Clinical Psychology Review, 73,* Article 101779. https://doi.org/10.1016/j.cpr.2019.101779

Tyler, K., Melander, L., & Almazan, E. (2010). Self injurious behavior among homeless young adults: A social stress analysis. *Social Science & Medicine, 70,* 269–276. https://doi.org/10.1016/j.socscimed.2009.10.008

Tyler, K. A., Whitbeck, L. B., Hoyt, D. R., & Johnson, K. D. (2003). Self-mutilation and homeless youth: The role of family abuse, street experiences, and mental disorders. *Journal of Research on Adolescence, 13,* 457–474. https://doi.org/10.1046/j.1532-7795.2003.01304003.x

U.S. Department of Housing and Urban Development. (2019, March 8). *HUD's definition of homelessness: Resources and guidance.* https://www.hudexchange.info/news/huds-definition-of-homelessness-resources-and-guidance

Sumaita Choudhury, MPH, *is a doctoral candidate and research associate, Texas Institute for Excellence in Mental Health, Steve Hicks School of Social Work, University of Texas at Austin, 1823 Red River Street, Austin, TX 78712, USA; email: sumaita.choudhury@austin.utexas.edu.* **Sharon Lee Choi, PhD,** *is a research associate;* **Yehyang Lee, MS,** *is a graduate research assistant; and* **Stacey Stevens Manser, PhD,** *is a research scientist and associate director, Texas Institute for Excellence in Mental Health, Steve Hicks School of Social Work, University of Texas at Austin,* Austin, TX, USA. *This study was funded through a contract with the Texas Health and Human Services Commission.*

Original manuscript received May 11, 2023
Final revision received August 17, 2023
Editorial decision September 7, 2023
Accepted September 8, 2023
Advance Access Publication March 13, 2024

NASW PRESS POLICY ON ETHICAL BEHAVIOR

The NASW Press expects authors to adhere to ethical standards for scholarship as articulated in the NASW *Code of Ethics* and *Writing for the NASW Press: Information for Authors.* These standards include actions such as

- taking responsibility and credit only for work they have actually performed
- honestly acknowledging the work of others
- submitting only original work to journals
- fully documenting their own and others' related work.

If possible breaches of ethical standards have been identified at the review or publication process, the NASW Press may notify the author and bring the ethics issue to the attention of the appropriate professional body or other authority. Peer review confidentiality will not apply where there is evidence of plagiarism.

As reviewed and revised by
NASW National Committee on
Inquiry (NCOI), May 30, 1997

Approved by NASW Board of
Directors, September 1997

Telehealth Use during COVID-19: An Exploratory Study on Adaptations and Experiences of Providers

Dana DeHart, Aidyn L. Iachini, Teri Browne, Melissa Reitmeier, and L. Bailey King

The current exploratory study examines the impact of the rapid acceleration of telehealth during the COVID-19 pandemic from the perspective of healthcare providers. Understanding provider perspectives, particularly in terms of adaptations made during this critical time, is a useful lens into service innovation in times of crisis and can help elucidate successful strategies for continuing the use of telehealth during the postpandemic period. Fourteen providers from 11 different service agencies in a southeastern state were interviewed. Findings identified three themes: (1) dynamic adaptations enacted by healthcare providers at the onset of the pandemic, such as hybrid services, rapid innovations in workflow, collective decision making among providers, and outreach to educate patients; (2) the relaxation of policies by regulators/insurers, focused most often on reimbursement of services; and (3) how patient engagement was impacted via telehealth, including openness to telehealth, more family-level accessibility, and reduced no-show rates. Implications for social workers include heightened professional training on telehealth as well as increasing the critical role that social workers serve in educating providers and patients on telehealth.

KEY WORDS: *adaptations; COVID-19; healthcare; telehealth*

The landscape of social services rapidly and dramatically shifted to telehealth use resulting from the devastating impact of the COVID-19 global pandemic. Despite minimal planning and preparation (Bashshur et al., 2020), the use of telehealth proliferated (Chang et al., 2021) and was necessitated as quarantines, citywide lockdowns, and social distancing mandates that were implemented in efforts to reduce transmission of the virus. Lieneck et al. (2021) describe the pandemic as a "flashpoint" for change, while Wosik et al. (2020) note that the pandemic "catalyzed rapid adoption of telehealth and transformed healthcare delivery at a breathtaking pace" (p. 957). This exploratory study aims to understand the impact of this rapid acceleration of telehealth during the COVID-19 pandemic from the perspective of healthcare providers who were on the frontlines of this crisis response. As telehealth use remains during this postpandemic landscape and other public health crises emerge, understanding such adaptations provides a useful lens into service innovation in times of crisis. The findings of this study can help elucidate successful strategies that could be utilized to help expand telehealth access and improve continuity of care, as well as help social workers and other healthcare professionals prepare and plan for future crisis response efforts.

TELEHEALTH

Telehealth is the use of telecommunications technologies to provide healthcare services, health education, and healthcare administration (Chang et al., 2021; Chen et al., 2021; Wosik et al., 2020). Telehealth enables virtual interactive communication between patients and providers and encompasses a wide variety of modalities that may be synchronous and/or asynchronous. *Synchronous telehealth* refers to direct communication between providers and patients at the same time, most commonly through phone or video consultations (Substance Abuse and Mental Health Services Administration [SAMHSA], 2021). *Asynchronous telehealth* refers to nonurgent means of healthcare provision that occur on the patient's and provider's own time, such as apps or computer programs that enable scheduling or appointment reminders or remote patient monitoring in which technologies collect health data that can then be transmitted to providers (SAMHSA, 2021).

Rapid Expansion of Telehealth during COVID-19

During the onset of the pandemic, telehealth was a necessity for maintaining continuity of care and a vital tool in efforts to overcome the shortage of safety equipment and healthcare personnel (Zorron Cheng Tao Pu et al., 2021). This method of care delivery also has allowed healthcare workers in high-risk groups to continue working safely while addressing the increasing demand for care (Gutierrez et al., 2021). Adepoju et al. (2021) examined telehealth use among healthcare administrators from primary care and specialty clinics and found that clinics transitioned to adopt telehealth quickly under pandemic conditions. In this study, clinics that delivered most of their consults via telehealth increased from 5 percent in February 2020 to 30 percent in June of the same year (Adepoju et al., 2021). Meyer et al. (2020) also examined adjustments to telehealth during the early months of COVID-19 in a single Wisconsin healthcare system and found that ambulatory care was reduced by 70 percent and acute care by 40 percent, but that billable telehealth visits from March to June 2020 were at a 1,700 percent increase relative to prepandemic levels. Lau et al. (2020) found in one New York hospital system that fewer than five hundred telehealth visits were billed monthly prior to the pandemic, but there were nearly 83,000 billable visits in a single month after the pandemic began. Even internationally, Tariq et al. (2021) identified rapid developments across countries, disciplines, and technologies during the pandemic, with some specialties that had previously been entirely in person (e.g., urology, hematology, dentistry) moving to virtual visits, remote patient monitoring, and even chatbots (i.e., computer programs that simulate human conversations) for screening and triage.

Impact of the Rapid Expansion of Telehealth during COVID-19

Several studies were conducted during the peak of the pandemic that explored the impacts associated with the rapid expansion of telehealth. For example, Wosik et al. (2020) noted that new strategies implemented at their healthcare institution included training all clinicians to provide both inpatient and outpatient care, and developing a centralized call center that was staffed by newly hired staff, repurposed staff, medical students, and persons highly experienced in use of telehealth. Loeb et al. (2020) also documented the experience of rapidly introducing telehealth over a five-day period in an orthopedic surgery unit at the onset of the pandemic. They noted adaptations needed such as developing a triage process to determine which patients could be served via telehealth and a checklist for launch of telemedicine, including categories of information technology (e.g., ensuring adequate bandwidth, confirming that cameras were working, obtaining backdrops), office management (e.g., developing templates), policy/credentialing (e.g., teaching providers to document visits), regulations (e.g., obtaining patient consent), and testing (e.g., simulated visits). In a study of specialty services, Peahl et al. (2020) described telehealth considerations within prenatal care during the COVID-19 pandemic, such as designing care around essential services that must be in person and creating flexible services so that patients can choose modalities to receive guidance and psychosocial support.

Many of the service and policy changes that had been implemented during the initial COVID-19 public health response remained widespread even after the emergency was lifted in May of 2023. These changes include greater flexibility in the types of services that can be reimbursed, what providers can prescribe via telehealth without an in-person assessment of patients, and provision of full Medicaid reimbursement of services if either the patient or the provider is on site (Knopf, 2023). Knopf (2023) notes that the changes became popular with both patients and providers, and that telehealth "continues to be broadly allowable" (p. 6) beyond the public health emergency. Thus, such shifts in service delivery appear to be enduring rather than isolated to the peak of the COVID-19 crisis. Understanding such shifts thereby allows a window into potential impacts of future crisis events on public health service and policy as well as strategies used by providers to adapt during these times of crisis.

CURRENT STUDY

Most of the studies to date that have explored this rapid expansion of telehealth due to COVID-19 have focused on single case examples or used a survey design. Yet, little is known qualitatively from a range of providers about their experiences during this critical time in healthcare. This exploratory study is designed to expand on existing studies by bringing forward the voices of healthcare providers through qualitative interviews and understanding the adaptations they made in relationship to telehealth as a result of the COVID-19 pandemic. As central providers in the delivery of telehealth services, provider perspectives are essential to understanding the three central research questions that guided this study: (1) What adaptations did providers make in service delivery upon onset of the pandemic? (2) What are providers' perspectives on policy shifts that resulted from the COVID-19 pandemic? and (3) What were providers' impressions of patient engagement in telehealth services during this crisis? Findings provide in-depth insights into the immediate impact of the pandemic on services, strategies that social workers and other providers can use to adapt, and how policymakers and patient adjustments were viewed by providers during this crisis.

METHOD

The current study was part of a broader telehealth implementation needs assessment in a southeastern state and was reviewed and exempted by a university human subjects review board.

Sampling

The funding agency, a university-affiliated state center on rural and primary healthcare, conducted an online survey of community-based providers' experiences with telehealth implementation. Interview participants for the current study were recruited from a convenience sample of interested survey participants. This sample included 14 providers from 11 agencies in South Carolina. Most provider agencies were located in metropolitan areas, but nearly all agencies served both rural and urban populations. Table 1 provides demographic information self-reported by the study participants.

Measures

Participants completed a demographic survey and were interviewed via Zoom during the fall of 2021. There were 11 total interviews. Most persons ($n = 9$) were interviewed individually by one of two staff interviewers, but additional staff attended group interviews at two agencies (group 1: $n = 3$, group 2: $n = 2$). Interviewers worked from a script of approximately 15 open-ended prompts addressing experiences and perspectives on telehealth prior to and throughout the COVID-19 pandemic. Examples included being asked to describe when and why their organization implemented

Table 1: Provider Demographic Characteristics ($N = 14$)

Demographic Variable	n	%
Gender		
Male	3	21.4
Female	11	78.6
Age (years)		
20–29	1	7.1
30–39	3	21.4
40–49	4	28.6
50–59	4	28.6
60–69	2	14.3
Race		
White	12	85.7
Black	2	14.3
Highest level of education		
Master's degree	13	92.9
Bachelor's degree	1	7.1
Field of practice		
Social work	5	35.9
Counseling or therapy	3	21.4
Health administration	3	21.4
Public health	1	7.1
Nursing	1	7.1
Special education	1	7.1
Practice setting		
Community nonprofit	4	28.6
Mental health services	4	28.6
Children's hospital	2	14.3
Hospital community services	2	14.3
Community health clinic	1	7.1
Veterans Health Administration	1	7.1
Time in practice (years)		
0–1	0	0.0
2–5	1	7.1
6–9	1	7.1
10–19	4	28.6
20+	8	57.2

telehealth, the types of telehealth services they offered to whom, challenges with telehealth implementation, the impact of the pandemic on their agency's use of telehealth, ideas on what would support telehealth use, and lessons learned from their experience. Interviews ranged from 35 to 126 minutes ($M = 59$ minutes) depending on the talkativeness of respondents as well as the depth of their experience with telehealth.

Analyses

Analyses of demographic data were conducted with SPSS (Version 26). Interviews were audio-recorded and transcribed. Qualitative content analyses were used to analyze the data within MaxQDA software (Cho & Lee, 2014; Schreier, 2012). First, we established a preliminary codebook of provisional codes guided by our interview prompts (Saldaña, 2009). Then, we used inductive open coding and paraphrasing of participant narratives to elucidate and describe emergent codes. We added these emergent codes to the provisional codebook, regularly checking and refining the boundaries of codes and maintaining each code's conceptual definition, inclusion and exclusion criteria, and typical/atypical exemplars (Guest & MacQueen, 2008).

Positionality and Trustworthiness

The research team included four faculty members and one staff member working at the University of South Carolina College of Social Work. All had extensive experience with program evaluation in health and social services, as well as prior experience conducting studies on provider use of telehealth. This experience contributed to strategies to promote trustworthiness. First, we established interview and analytic methods and built on our team's previous qualitative research on telehealth use (DeHart, Iachini, et al., 2022; DeHart, King, et al., 2022). Frequent team reflections and iterative data coding provided additional opportunities to refine codes and thoroughly describe our conclusions in connection to the raw data. While members of the research team did not have prolonged interaction with participating providers, the funding organization did have prior professional interactions with these providers. Providers willingly chose to participate and were not identified to the funding agency by the research team, promoting genuine and forthright responses. Characteristics of the sample (see demographics in Table 1) are reported to enable a better understanding of the context of the findings (Shenton, 2004). Themes discussed herein are those with wide coverage across the dataset as well as those of practical significance for shaping future research, practice, and policy. Some quotes have been minimally edited for increased clarity and to remove identifying speech patterns (e.g., "you know").

RESULTS

Three themes emerged from the study: (1) dynamic adaptations enacted by providers at the onset of the pandemic, (2) relaxation of policies by regulators/insurers, and (3) patient engagement via telehealth.

Dynamic Adaptations Enacted by Providers at the Onset of the Pandemic

Of the 11 agencies represented in our study, the majority ($n = 7$) had already been using telehealth prior to the COVID-19 pandemic. The remaining four agencies shifted services to telehealth during the pandemic. While we examined the data for differences among these two groups, no major differences were identified in the application of codes across transcripts from those providers who had previously used telehealth versus those who had not.

Panic and Leveling Up Technology. It is interesting to note that prior experience with telehealth did not insulate agencies from a sense of crisis upon realization that a pandemic may necessitate a dramatic shift in service delivery from in person to telehealth. Providers used words such as "nervous," "frantic," and "desperation" in describing their reactions. For example, one shared:

> That first week or two weeks [were a] little chaotic. . . . We didn't have enough cameras, we didn't have microphones, we didn't have enough computers for people who were working at home, we had to set up licenses for a variety of different software platforms. (Provider 12)

Indeed, technological adaptations took some time to implement, and some providers had to halt or delay services—primarily as a temporary measure while agency staff tried to troubleshoot logistical issues for telehealth service deliveries.

> We did have about a two-month lapse in groups, mainly because groups have some additional challenges like privacy. . . . Our groups are unstructured—an open group so anyone in the community can join. But we'd heard horror stories about Zoom-bombing happening, and we want to make sure that while they're open, we also can somewhat control the environment. (Provider 11)

Moving from panic and technical scaling to manageable service delivery was an iterative process that intersected with dynamic adaptations to meet the challenges of the pandemic.

Flexible Delivery Options. Providers described using hybrid service delivery models in which some services were delivered in person while others were delivered through digital platforms. This included service delivery through large and small practices and with both children and adult patients. One provider noted:

> Prior to COVID, we had a little bit more rule-outs in terms of who we would recommend telehealth for. So for some of our kids, we would typically recommend seven or eight and up. But when the clinics had to shut down, and we had four- and five-year-olds. . . . We had to kind of figure out how to make that work. (Provider 11)

Providers tried to promote continuity of care by offering flexibility to patients, which sometimes required some adjustment from providers' typical protocols, age restrictions, and service preferences.

Rapid Innovation. Pandemic conditions created new workflow needs, both around scale of telehealth delivery and in problem solving around the difficult situations, as noted by one provider:

> A big portion of that program was school based. So of course, all [public] schools closed, and that displaced all of those staff. . . . We turned those staff into—and they're nurses, medical assistants—they were like triage lines. And so they were taking the incoming calls, educating patients on telehealth, setting them up with either some of our nurse practitioners in the school program who were displaced or practitioners in the office—because the office numbers were down. (Provider 7)

Providers thereby applied their skills in new ways as demands on-site and off-site changed, sometimes taking on roles they had not exercised previously. They discovered that the telehealth platforms often required more rigorous planning. As one provider notes, the crisis situation pressed providers to identify solutions to a range of problems, in some instances, strengthening the overall service model:

> Even with us having so much experience, we have created much more strong curriculums in telehealth—a lot more lessons learned that I think we would have eventually gotten. But having to transition to all tele all the time, especially with our higher-risk populations, I think forced us to get really creative really fast, [and] I think ultimately made our services better. (Provider 11)

In this way, telehealth served as a prod, pushing providers to think more critically about how to provide services in a way that was accessible and meaningful to patients. This required moving from "business as usual" to less familiar, more innovative strategies.

Collective Decision Making. Providers discussed working collaboratively, both within and across agencies, to develop innovative ideas for moving services forward.

> In my office, everyone came in here every day during COVID unless someone was sick. . . . We would go, "OK, what happens today? Who's out? Who's in? Who's where? What's up with this kid? Where's the money? How do you get PPE [personal protective equipment]? Where's the stuff? How am I getting a mask?" This was the emergency center in my office. We were here troubleshooting every day pretty much something. (Provider 2)

Providers often described these collaborative experiences as strengthening intra- and interagency bonds with colleagues.

> I think it's just taught us so much about relationships and our staff and our team and our leadership—and the resilience of our staff, for people to show up every day. We gave people the option to, "All right, do you want to leave, or do you want to stay? Because if you're staying, we're all in. (Provider 2)

Thus, the mutual commitment to be "all in" helped providers come together to troubleshoot, jointly identify solutions, and come together to better serve patients.

Patient Outreach and Support. One of the easier adaptations that providers enacted involved reaching out to patients to inform them of service changes or promote flexible new options. One provider described the outreach conducted around their triage call center.

> These core people knew all about telehealth. They knew how to use the apps. They could educate the patients.... And so we pushed that out, we put it on our website. We did a lot of flyers. We were doing a lot of COVID testing events at the time—so like drive-through events and big, big events. So that was in the packet that patients received. They received, like, COVID information, testing information. (Provider 7)

Thus, providers reached out not just in efforts to continue delivery of routine services, but also to increase patient knowledge around the pandemic, testing, and telehealth in general. This likely helped facilitate uptake of telehealth for patients and communities.

Relaxation of Policies by Regulators and/or Insurers

Providers at eight of the agencies described impacts of regulators or insurers relaxing policies around telehealth delivery during COVID-19, typically framing this in a positive light. Foremost, providers discussed their ability to offer services via telehealth that were not previously reimbursed by insurers.

> It's a yearly visit. It's an anticipatory guidance, preventive care, education visit, coordination of care, just basically a well checkup. And so we had done those previously on our mobile units, we would go to the schools, pull the children out of class, and we would do those visits. So when schools closed, we kind of pivoted to telehealth.... Medicaid came out and said that they would cover the wellness visit with the idea that as soon as a visit in person was safe, that you would do the physical portion of the exam that you couldn't do via telehealth. So we began doing [that].... I hope that is something that Medicaid does not go back on because that's really been helpful for our kids.... It's interesting to do their well visit via telehealth versus in person because you get so much more information when someone's in their home and comfortable and

speaking to you than sitting in a cold, weird-looking doctor's office. (Provider 7)

Thus, relaxation of policies not only increased continuity of care, but also created conditions through which providers gained insight into more natural home and family dynamics of their patients. Another provider expressed concern over ambiguity about whether reimbursements could continue to deliver these services.

> [The] writing on the wall of long-term adoption [of these policies] is just really getting support of, like, CMS [Centers for Medicare & Medicaid Services] and local legislature in terms of reimbursements, I think [it] is going to be where it's really going to reflect if telehealth can be here to stay.... I've been going to the statehouse for every year to advocate on behalf of Medicaid expansion to cover telehealth, and we get shut down pretty much every year. I think it's gonna be harder for things to not eventually get passed, because this past year has really shown that it's actually cost saving. And people can get seen. So I think there's still going to be probably a pushback to it, but... I'm more hopeful... because so many providers and patients alike have adopted telehealth and seen the benefits. I think it's gonna be harder to kind of just like shove us back to pre-COVID times. (Provider 11)

It was evident to providers that patients may not fully comprehend the intricacies of reimbursement policies, should they be reversed. For instance, Medicaid policies had been relaxed to allow for service delivery when *either* the patient or doctor was on site in the office (Knopf, 2023), which previously had been disallowed in some circumstances, forcing patients to travel to a satellite office where they would then receive telehealth services from a provider in a different office location. Once patients and providers became accustomed to the new, more flexible guidelines, they welcomed these and were concerned about longevity of changes. For the time being, as of summer 2023, many such flexible policies still exist (Knopf, 2023), but this should be an issue of note to social workers and others who may face adjustments to the guidelines going forward.

Patient Engagement via Telehealth

As access to services improved, whether patients were equally engaged in services could be debatable. However, providers at 10 of the 11 agencies mentioned some positive impacts on patient engagement via telehealth. Foremost, they noted that patients who may have never considered telehealth were now quite open to it:

> When we started a new program and we started getting the consents, we at least had that feedback from parents saying, "Oh yeah, I kind of know what this is." . . . We don't really do any marketing or advertising around it, because really the trends right now in both the state, the nation, everything, you can't turn on the TV without hearing the word "telehealth," so that kind of does the work for us. (Provider 5)

Thus, as school coursework, workplace meetings, social gatherings, concerts, and varied other routinely in-person interactions went online at the peak of the pandemic, patients, families, and communities were becoming more welcoming to virtual engagement. Providers underscored heightened involvement of families in services due to telehealth during the pandemic:

> We did try to look on the bright side, because we're "rose colored–wearing glasses" optimists. Family involvement over the summer went better. We had more family involvement for kids in schools than we do regularly. And obviously, that's a reflection of the kids [being] at home, the parents [being] at home, it's a lot easier to get all of them involved in the setting. So we had higher rates of family therapy than we ever had during the summer. (Provider 12)

As with wellness visits for children, the family presence in the home became an asset to family-oriented service interventions. Another benefit for engagement may have involved the convenience of virtual services cutting away travel commitments. One provider noted changes in no-show rates for patients:

> In trauma treatment, typically we have about a 60 percent no-show rate, if you look at the national data for trauma treatment. And this

year, we've had about an 80 percent show rate. So we've reduced our no-show rate pretty significantly. (Provider 11)

Trauma treatment might be conceived as a triggering experience for some who dreaded prolonged deliberation about the trauma during drives to and from providers, while sitting in the waiting room, and in other aspects of the visit. The telehealth platforms seemed to attenuate this for some. Several providers noted that telehealth during the pandemic led to new patients, particularly due to geographic access:

> Now I talk to families from all over. . . . Families email me from all over about how to build a community for people with disabilities, and I get to talk to them, helping them in all different states, which is so nice. (Provider 2)

Thus, our provider sample noted many potential therapeutic benefits stemming from convenience for patients and their families.

DISCUSSION

This exploratory study sought to understand the impact of the rapid acceleration of telehealth during the COVID-19 pandemic from the perspective of healthcare providers. Findings illustrate a number of dynamic adaptations made by providers at the onset of the pandemic, the relaxation of policies and regulations that occurred during this time, and provider insights regarding patient engagement. While most providers had utilized telehealth prior to the pandemic, this use did not insulate providers from crisis impacts, particularly around the need to scale up telehealth use rapidly during the pandemic's onset. Many providers had to halt or delay services while troubleshooting problems, and managing services within the crisis was an iterative process of problem solving and service delivery. Providers innovated, allowing flexible service options for patients, including in-person, remote, and hybrid services as well as diverse platforms for service delivery. Rapid innovations included having to shift staff roles, creating triage centers, performing patient education, and developing solutions for some problems that had already existed prior to the pandemic (e.g., transportation, educational formats). Collective decision making was used daily to address crises, and professionals worked across disciplines for education and outreach. Media solutions, drive-through events, and virtual meeting places were established to support patients. These findings support previous studies in that agencies and providers appear to be highly adaptable in crises such as these (Adepoju et al., 2021), with the pandemic acting as a flashpoint that prompted change (Lieneck et al., 2021), both for providers and patients. As noted by Wosik et al. (2020), repurposing staff as the workplace and work demands changed became an essential adaptation strategy, as did direct-patient marketing (Loeb et al., 2020).

In this study, providers also described the importance of the relaxation of policies and regulations around the provision of telehealth and how that impacted service delivery, echoing concerns in recent literature that service access may suffer if the relaxed policies enacted during the pandemic are reversed. As noted, many policies around reimbursement have persisted, but some of the policy shifts are still under temporary holds that could be reversed pending public comment and studies of implications (Knopf, 2023). Meyer and colleagues (2020) assert that if temporary regulatory adjustments are not made permanent, vulnerable healthcare systems may suffer from reduced flexibility. Peahl et al. (2020) also advocate for policy changes to include payer reimbursement for telehealth technologies such as remote monitoring devices, arguing that sustaining these care options can help address health disparities and allow providers to meet patients where they are in homes, workplaces, and communities. Future research should continue to examine whether temporary policy adjustments have been effective and examine clinical outcomes of different types of visits so that reimbursement rates do not create a system in which video technology is incentivized over telephone encounters if both are equally effective (Segel et al., 2021; Wosik et al., 2020).

Providers in this study also felt that the necessity of telehealth had drawn in patients who otherwise would not have tried it, and the virtual format allowed for geographic expansion of the patient base. They also noted that family engagement was enhanced via virtual services, and some providers experienced a reduction in no-show appointments. Bashshur et al. (2020) believe acceptance of telehealth may be rooted in widespread dependence on virtual technology in all sectors of society, empirical evidence of telehealth's effectiveness, public awareness of its benefits during the pandemic, and positive attitudes among clinicians who now have firsthand experience with telehealth. During this postpandemic landscape, there have been substantial changes in everyday technology use by patients and families, likely alleviating some of the barriers to care we have identified previously (DeHart, Iachini, et al., 2022) and elucidating the changes to engagement we discuss here.

Limitations

Several limitations to the study must be noted. The findings are limited to a small sample of counseling centers, clinics, and hospitals in a single southeastern state. We did not systematically assess certain contextual variables, such as provider funding sources (i.e., government, nonprofit, or private) or percentage of patients from rural/urban locales, which could impact findings and are important avenues for future inquiry around telehealth use. Further, our prompts were focused on general experiences, challenges, and lessons learned rather than tapping into specific innovations. Further research might delve deeper into the range and nature of innovations enacted by a broader, geographically diverse sample of providers.

Also, our sample was recruited from a pool of providers who had already completed an online survey. This, plus the study's reliance on distance technologies for interviewing providers, likely biased the sample toward those providers who were more comfortable using virtual platforms such as SurveyMonkey and Zoom. Future studies might garner more representative samples by combining both virtual and in-person interviewing with a random sample of providers. While the research team and a plurality of provider participants were social workers, our conclusions regarding implications for social work might be strengthened or diversified by sampling exclusively social workers from a range of healthcare settings. Researchers might also examine perspectives of patients as they experience these innovations. Performance data from healthcare systems may also attest to the impact these adaptations have on agency outcomes, including financial viability, patient engagement, and physical and psychological well-being.

Implications for Social Work Practice

Despite these limitations and the need for future research in this area, there are several important implications for social work practice. First, social workers should be trained, be prepared, and utilize telehealth within their scope of practice. Given the commitment of the profession to serve vulnerable populations, considering how telehealth can help address health equity is critical. Likewise, social workers also need to be aware of broadband access issues that can impede the use of telehealth, particularly in rural areas (DeHart, King, et al., 2022) and need to advocate for policies that support internet expansion into remote and rural areas. Additionally, social workers are instrumental in crisis planning and preparedness. As such, social workers should examine current crisis plans for their agency settings and examine how current processes map onto findings of recent studies around what adaptations supported telehealth use during this crisis.

Overall, the adaptability of healthcare agencies to meet the rapid need and demand for telehealth was remarkable. Through the resilience demonstrated by healthcare systems in response to the pandemic and learning from healthcare providers who experienced this from the frontlines, we can continue to enrich our understanding of the best ways to scale up telehealth and prepare for future crises. **HSW**

REFERENCES

Adepoju, O., Chae, M., Ayadi, F., Matuk-Villazon, O., & Liaw, W. (2021). Early impacts of the COVID-19 pandemic on telehealth patterns in primary care, mental health, and specialty care facilities in Texas. *Southern Medical Journal, 114*, 593–596.

Bashshur, R. L., Doarn, C. R., Frenk, J. M., Kvedar, J. C., Shannon, G. W., & Woolliscroft, J. O. (2020). Beyond the COVID pandemic, telemedicine, and health care. *Telemedicine Journal and e-Health, 26*, 131–1313. https://doi.org/10.1089/tmj.2020.0328

Chang, J. E., Lai, A. Y., Gupta, A., Nguyen, A. M., Berry, C. A., & Shelley, D. R. (2021). Rapid transition to telehealth and the digital divide: Implications for primary care access and equity in a post-COVID era. *Milbank Quarterly, 99*, 340–368.

Chen, J., Amaize, A., & Barath, D. (2021). Evaluating telehealth adoption and related challenges among hospitals located in rural and urban areas. *Journal of Rural Health, 37*, 801–811. https://doi.org/10.1111/jrh.12534

Cho, J. Y., & Lee, E. H. (2014). Reducing confusion about grounded theory and qualitative content analysis: Similarities and differences. *Qualitative Report, 19*, Article 2. https://doi.org/10.46743/2160-3715/2014.1028

DeHart, D., Iachini, A., King, L. B., LeCleir, E., Reitmeier, M., & Browne, T. (2022). Benefits and challenges of telehealth use during COVID-19: Perspectives of patients and providers in the rural South. *Advances in Social Work, 22*, 953–975.

DeHart, D., King, L. B., Iachini, A. L., Browne, T., & Reitmeier, M. (2022). Benefits and challenges of implementing telehealth in rural settings: A mixed-methods study of behavioral medicine providers. *Health & Social Work, 47*, 7–18.

Guest, G., & MacQueen, K. (2008). *Handbook for team-based qualitative research.* Altamira.

Gutierrez, J., Kuperman, E., & Kaboli, P. J. (2021). Using telehealth as a tool for rural hospitals in the COVID-19 pandemic response. *Journal of Rural Health, 37*, 161–164.

Knopf, A. (2023). Telehealth reimbursement by Medicaid continues. *Alcoholism & Drug Abuse Weekly, 35*, 5–6.

Lau, J., Knudsen, J., Jackson, H., Wallach, A. B., Bouton, M., Natsui, S., Philippou, C., Karim, E., Silvestri, D. M., Avalone, L., Zaurova, M., Schatz, D., Sun, V., & Chokshi, D. A. (2020). Staying connected in the COVID-19 pandemic: Telehealth at the largest safety-net system in the United States. *Health Affairs, 39*, 1437–1442.

Lieneck, C., Weaver, E., & Maryon, T. (2021). Outpatient telehealth implementation in the United States during the COVID-19 global pandemic: A systematic review. *Medicina, 57*, 462–479.

Loeb, A. E., Rao, S. S., Ficke, J. R., Morris, C. D., Riley, L. H., III, & Levin, A. S. (2020). Departmental experience and lessons learned with accelerated introduction of telemedicine during the COVID-19 crisis. *Journal of the American Academy of Orthopedic Surgery, 28*, E469–E476.

Meyer, C., Becot, F., Burke, R., & Weichelt, B. (2020). Rural telehealth use during the COVID-19 pandemic: How long-term infrastructure commitment may support rural health care systems resilience. *Journal of Agromedicine, 25*, 362–366.

Peahl, A. F., Smith, R. D., & Moniz, M. H. (2020). Prenatal care redesign: Creating flexible maternity care models through virtual care. *American Journal of Obstetrics and Gynecology, 223*, 389.e1–389.e10.

Saldaña, J. (2009). *The coding manual for qualitative researchers.* SAGE.

Schreier, M. (2012). *Qualitative content analysis in practice.* SAGE.

Segel, J., Ross, H., Edwards, J., Braun, K., & Davis, L. (2021). The unique challenges facing rural providers in the COVID-19 pandemic. *Population Health Management, 24*, 304–306.

Shenton, A. (2004). Strategies for ensuring trustworthiness in qualitative research projects. *Education for Information, 22*, 63–75.

Substance Abuse and Mental Health Services Administration. (2021). *Advisory: Using technology-based therapeutic tools in behavioral health services* (Publication No. PEP20-06-04-001). https://store.samhsa.gov/product/advisory-using-technology-based-therapeutic-tools-behavioral-health-services-based-tip-60

Tariq, A., Aziz, O., Arain, F., & Munir, M. (2021). COVID-19 compels practitioners and governments to promote telemedicine practices: A systematic review. *Applied Medical Informatics, 43*, 68–80.

Wosik, J., Fudim, M., Cameron, B., Gellad, Z. F., Cho, A., Phinney, D., Curtis, S., Roman, M., Poon, E. G., Ferranti, J., Katz, J. N., & Tcheng, J. (2020). Telehealth transformation: COVID-19 and the rise of virtual care. *Journal of the American Medical Informatics Association, 27*, 957–962. https://doi.org/10.1093/jamia/ocaa067

Zorron Cheng Tao Pu, L., Raval, M., Terbah, R., Singh, G., Rajadurai, A., Vaughan, R., Efthymiou, M., & Chandran, S. (2021). Video consultations during the coronavirus disease 2019 pandemic are associated with high satisfaction for both doctors and patients. *Journal of Gastroenterology and Hepatology, 5*, 542–548. https://doi.org/10.1002/jgh3.12547

Dana DeHart, PhD, *is research professor emerita, College of Social Work, University of South Carolina, 332 Hamilton College, Columbia, SC 29208, USA; email: dana.dehart@ sc.edu.* ***Aidyn L. Iachini, PhD, MSW,*** *is associate dean for research and faculty;* ***Teri Browne, PhD, NSW-C,*** *is dean; and* ***Melissa Reitmeier, PhD, LMSW,*** *is clinical professor, College of Social Work, University of South Carolina, Columbia, SC, USA.* ***L. Bailey King, MSW,*** *is manager of corporate and foundation partnerships, The Mission Continues, Atlanta, GA, USA.*

Original manuscript received March 23, 2023
Final revision received August 7, 2023
Editorial decision September 7, 2023
Accepted September 7, 2023
Advance Access Publication March 9, 2024

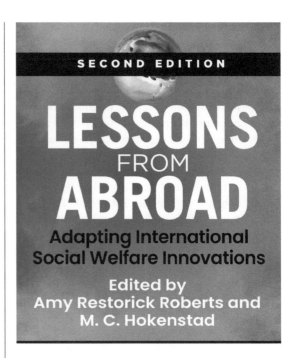

GIVE US YOUR POINT OF VIEW!

Viewpoint submissions, which go through the normal peer review process, should be no longer than seven double-spaced pages. Send your Viewpoint column as a Word document through the online portal at http://hsw. msubmit.net (initial, one-time registration is required).

There is much to learn through the international exchange of policy initiatives and program models. In the second edition of *Lessons from Abroad*, editors Amy Restorick Roberts and M. C. "Terry" Hokenstad bring together top scholars who share their expertise about approaches for understanding and addressing an array of global challenges through policy and practice examples from both developing and developed countries. Some chapters examine distinct content areas, such as child welfare, aging, the climate crisis, and forced migration. Other chapters more broadly address global issues directly aligned with the values and professional ethics of social work, including environmental justice, the alleviation of poverty, social security, and community development.

ISBN: 978-0-87101-578-5. 2022.
Item #5785. 204 pages. 1-800-227-3590
www.naswpress.org

APLFA22

Piloting a Community-Based, Culturally Adapted Health Promotion Program for Children with Autism Spectrum Disorder and Developmental Disabilities in First-Generation Korean Immigrant Families

Esther Son and Sabretta Alford

Children with autism spectrum disorder and developmental disabilities (ASD/DD) face barriers to participation in health promotion programs due to the lack of available and/or affordable programs and trained staff at recreation centers. Children with ASD/DD in Korean immigrant families are one of the most underserved minority groups due to language, racial/ethnic discrimination, and stigma and shame within their own ethnic community. However, little research is available on development, implementation, and evaluation of a culturally adapted community health promotion program in this population. The purpose of this study is to assess effectiveness of a pilot program for children with ASD/DD from first-generation Korean immigrant families. The pilot study used a quantitative, quasiexperimental design (one-group design with pre- and posttest) following a seven-week health promotion program. We recruited 15 children with ASD/DD, ages nine through 16, from first-generation Korean immigrant families. The findings of the study suggest that the pilot program was effective in gaining nutrition knowledge and increasing physical involvement among participants. Given the fact that Asian immigrants are a fast-growing population and that nearly 75 percent of them were born abroad, development and evaluation of a community-based, culturally adapted health promotion program is urgently needed.

KEY WORDS: *children with autism spectrum disorder/developmental disabilities; first-generation Korean immigrant families; health promotion; prevention*

Overweight and obesity represent major public health problems for children and adults with autism spectrum disorder and developmental disabilities (ASD/DD) compared with the general population (Curtin et al., 2010; Egan et al., 2013; J. H. Rimmer et al., 2010). The majority of studies suggest that the risk for overweight/obesity is higher among children with ASD/DD (Hinckson et al., 2013; Matheson & Douglas, 2017; Zuckerman et al., 2014). For example, one of the principal features of ASD is habitual and stereotypic food preferences, which may lead to excess intake of saturated fats and refined sugars (Bandini et al., 2010; Hubbard et al., 2014; Suarez & Crinion, 2015; Zimmer et al., 2012). As children with ASD grow, they gain more autonomy in food choices and increased access to energy-dense snacks that can lead to overweight and obesity. However, choices in food repertoire (number of unique foods eaten) are difficult to change among children with ASD/DD, supporting the need for interventions early in childhood to increase the variety and promote healthy eating among children with ASD/DD (Bandini et al., 2010; Bandini et al., 2017).

The umbrella term "DD" originates early in life and refers to functional limitations in cognition and/or mobility and other independent living skills. Examples of DD include ASD, attention-deficit/hyperactivity disorder, seizures, cerebral palsy, Down syndrome, and intellectual disabilities (ID; Schalock et al., 2009). Children with ASD/DD also have lower fitness levels and higher rates of sedentary behaviors than those of typically developing children

(Golubović et al., 2012; Matheson & Douglas, 2017; J. H. Rimmer et al., 2010). The association between physical activity and wellness is well established in the general population, yet individuals with ASD/DD have difficulty maintaining the higher activity levels necessary to ensure a healthier life (Haveman et al., 2010; Lynch et al., 2022), and weight loss studies typically exclude children with ASD/DD (Matheson & Douglas, 2017). Nevertheless, previous studies show that increased physical activity in the ASD/DD population can have multiple positive effects on health and well-being. For example, increasing physical activity of children with ASD/DD can improve motor coordination (Memari et al., 2017), cardiovascular fitness (Menear & Neumeier, 2015), social behavior/interaction (Gregor et al., 2018; Huang et al., 2020), communication skills (Huang et al., 2020; Yarimkaya et al., 2017), and stress levels (Hillier et al., 2011). Huang and colleagues (2020) recently conducted a meta-analysis on the effects of physical activity programs on children and adolescents with ASD. Results indicated that physical activity programs had a favorable influence on social interaction, motor skills, and communication skills of adolescents with ASD. Other studies confirm that increasing physical activity participation in structured programs can positively impact social interaction and communication skills among children with ASD/DD (Hinckson et al., 2013; Srinivasan et al., 2014; Zhao & Chen, 2018). These findings highlight the critical importance of developing and evaluating health promotion programs for this population.

There are also programs targeting changes in physical activity and nutrition behaviors in overweight and obese children with ASD/DD (Hinckson et al., 2013; Suarez-Balcazar et al., 2016) that are shown to be more effective when they are customizable and culturally tailored. Hinckson and colleagues (2013) examined physical activity and nutrition interventions for overweight and obese children with ASD/DD. Twenty-two children and their families participated in a 10-week school-based intervention program in New Zealand. Data were collected at the beginning, at completion (post-1), and at the 24-week follow-up (post-2) and included level of fitness with a six-minute walk test, level of body fat using a standard waist measurement, and calculation of body mass index (BMI). Interviews with parents were used to measure nutrition changes and physical activity. After 24 weeks (post-2), researchers noted improved endurance among participants. In addition, 80 percent of parents reported that children reduced their consumption of sweets to once a week or less. Parents also noted fewer school absences related to illness, and teachers perceived that the participants were more active and aware of healthy food choices. These results suggest that children with ASD/DD and their families can make healthy diet and physical activity changes when encouraged. Recently, researchers explored novel interventions to promote health and well-being among children with ASD/DD. Healy and Marchand (2020) used a web-based, parent-mediated physical activity program to determine the feasibility and outcome of physical health education in children with ASD. The intervention program, Project CHASE, consisted of parents joining a private Facebook group where they were exposed to five intervention components. Parents completed a questionnaire measuring perceived effectiveness and engagement before and after the intervention. Results revealed that parents were satisfied or very satisfied with the intervention and that Project CHASE effectively supported their child's physical activity. Most participants actively engaged in reporting weekly goals, levels of physical activity, and information on physical activity opportunities. Many parents posted pictures of their child's activities. These findings suggest that web-based intervention programs can be valuable in promoting physical activities for children with ASD.

Despite the clear benefits of health promotion programs/interventions, however, children with disabilities are more restricted in their participation due to the lack of widespread availability of these types of programs (J. A. Rimmer & Rowland, 2008). Children with ASD/DD face various environmental and attitudinal barriers to maintaining a healthy lifestyle, which can put them at risk for overweight/obesity and chronic diseases as adults (Bandini et al., 2013; Matheson & Douglas, 2017; Suarez-Balcazar et al., 2016). These barriers to participation in health promotion programs are due to a combination of limited accessibility, lack of affordable programs, and untrained staff at recreation centers. These children may be less likely to join a community or recreational sports league or structured physical activity and nutrition program due to stigma and shame toward people with disabilities and their families in their community. Thus, they may have less opportunity to engage in physical activity and nutrition programs. Furthermore, children with ASD/DD may prefer not to play with their neighbors or peers after school and on the weekends due to negative attitudes and discrimination toward people with disabilities. As such, it may require additional intervention to engage in social and physically active outlets (Matheson & Douglas, 2017).

While the need for interventions that promote healthy lifestyles in the ASD/DD population is increasingly clear (Hinckson & Curtis, 2013), it is less certain that these programs can be readily adapted to children from immigrant families facing challenges from cultural, language, and institutional barriers (Magaña et al., 2021). Asians are among the fastest-growing immigrant population in the United States, and they recently passed Hispanics as the largest group of new immigrants (Lee & Sheng, 2024). However, Koreans are only one of the top six ethnic groups of Asian immigrants (Lopez et al., 2015), indicating the complexities in studying lifestyle interventions in Asian subgroups with ASD/DD (Sritharan & Koola, 2019). Children in first-generation Korean immigrant families with ASD/DD are a largely underserved ethnic group. The prevalence of overweight in children with DD was almost five times higher compared with the general population in South Korea (Ha et al., 2010). Asian immigrant families face multiple barriers to participation in health promotion programs, including lack of time due to work schedules, lack of language proficiency, and shame and stigma within their community (Son et al., 2018). DD research, particularly for ASD research, has limited empirical evidence on the experiences and needs specific to racial/ethnic subgroups, despite evidence of racial/ethnic disparities in health outcomes (West et al., 2016). The study's focus on Asian subgroups is vital as extant literature often dichotomizes race (White vs. non-White) or presents Asian populations as a monolith. Therefore, the purpose of this study is to assess the effectiveness of a pilot program for children with ASD/DD from first-generation Korean immigrant families and to test the following two hypotheses: (1) Children with ASD/DD who participated in the health promotion program would reduce their weight. (2) Children with ASD/DD who participated in the health promotion program would gain increased nutrition knowledge. We modified, both culturally and linguistically, a health promotion intervention originally developed for Latino youth with disabilities and their families (Suarez-

Balcazar et al., 2016), as well as a nutrition curriculum designed for teenagers (Bandini et al., 2013).

METHOD
Research Design, Participants, and Procedure

This pilot study used a quantitative, quasiexperimental design (one-group design with pre- and posttest). Fifteen children with ASD/DD, ages nine through 16, were recruited from first-generation Korean immigrant families who speak Korean at home and eat Korean food daily, and were provided with a seven-week health promotion program that included an hour-long nutrition education session and an hour-long physical activity session. The program started in October 2019 and ended in December 2019 at a community-based agency providing a wide range of information, support, and assistance to Korean immigrant families. The protocol was approved by the institutional review board of our university. The participants were recruited in collaboration with staff from a community-based agency in New York serving children with ASD/DD from Korean-immigrant families. Potential participants and their families received a letter of invitation explaining the project in detail. Signed informed consent was obtained from the participants' caregivers. An effort was made to ensure that each participant understood the project and actively chose whether to participate.

The ages of the participants ranged from nine to 16. Demographic characteristics are presented in Table 1. Most participants were male (80 percent) and had ASD (73 percent). The participants' mean age was 13 years old, height was 60 inches, weight was 113 pounds, BMI score was 22, and BMI-for-age was at the 66th percentile. Specifically, 33 percent of the participants had unhealthy weight (one overweight and four obese). The prevalence of overweight and obesity among the participants was similar to previous studies focusing on children with ASD/DD (Hinckson et al., 2013; Matheson & Douglas, 2017).

Program

The health promotion program consisted of a seven-week health and nutrition intervention modified from previously published research (Bandini et al., 2013; Suarez-Balcazar et al., 2016). Materials were modified culturally and linguistically by the research team, which consisted of the principal investigator, a social worker, social work student volunteers, a nutritionist, and a

Table 1: Description of Study Participants (*N* = 15)

Baseline Characteristic	*n*	%	*M (SD)*	Percentile
Gender				
Male	12	80		
Female	3	20		
Diagnosis				
ASD	11	73		
Down syndrome	3	20		
Intellectual disability	1	7		
Age (years)			13 (2.52)	
Height (in)			60 (5.50)	
Weight (lb)			113 (34.99)	
BMI			22 (5.31)	
BMI-for-age				66th

Notes: ASD = autism spectrum disorders; BMI = body mass index.

sports/yoga instructor (see Appendix for details about the program). The health promotion program was implemented as part of a free Saturday community-based program for children with ASD/DD. Participants met once a week for two hours. The facility is equipped with classrooms, a kitchen, and a large indoor gym, allowing for health and nutrition education and physical activity. Each of the seven sessions covered two components: nutrition education and physical activity. The program comprised one hour of health and nutrition education, focusing on children with ASD/DD only learning to make and eat a healthy snack, and one hour of physical activities, including warm-up, stretching, strengthening, conditioning, and basketball drills/yoga, led by a sports/yoga instructor. We introduced simple activities, progressed to complex ones, including those that were enjoyable, and utilized the individuals' interests and strengths when designing a physical activity program. Each session culminated with an educational discussion of healthy eating habits and moderate to vigorous physical activity. Several cultural adaptations were made to align with the target population's cultural norms. For example, we used a variety of culturally appropriate foods (i.e., Korean food) to introduce the "MyPlate" model and made healthy Korean snacks during the program.

Measures

Measurements at Baseline and Postintervention. Data were collected at baseline (preintervention)

and at nine to 10 weeks (postintervention). Socio-demographic data for the participants were collected before the program. Preintervention data included children's height, weight, and BMI, and nutrition knowledge among children with ASD/DD. Participants' BMI and the corresponding BMI-for-age percentile were calculated based on Centers for Disease Control and Prevention (CDC, n.d.) growth charts for children and teens ages two through 19 years. Similar postintervention data were collected between nine and 10 weeks after the program began.

Outcome Variables. Children's weight status (BMI and BMI-for-age percentile) was measured before and after the program. As opposed to adults, weight status in children is categorized using age- and sex-adjusted percentiles, such that the overweight category encompasses children in the 85th–95th BMI percentiles, whereas obesity is defined as a BMI equal to or greater than the 95th percentile. We used the BMI Percentile Calculator for Child and Teen, which provides BMI and the corresponding BMI-for-age percentile based on CDC (n.d.) growth charts for children and teens ages two through 19 years. In order to assess the child's nutritional knowledge, a 12-item survey was used to test their understanding of MyPlate and healthy food choices, including culturally appropriate foods used in the program pre- and postintervention. MyPlate is a food guidance symbol and the latest nutrition guide from the U.S. Department of Agriculture (USDA) that is used in nutrition education in the United States. The graphic depicts a place setting with a plate and glass divided into five food groups (fruits, vegetables, grains, protein, and dairy) recommended for a healthy diet. Each food group includes a variety of foods and plays an essential role in an overall healthy eating pattern (Chang, 2017). The survey consists of 12 questions asking about the components of MyPlate and food group and healthy food choice quizzes (e.g., "What are the five food groups?"; "What should half MyPlate be filled with?"; and "There are many different kinds of protein foods. Which of these are not included in protein foods?")

Data Analysis

To examine the effectiveness of the health promotion program, the data were analyzed using SPSS (Version 25). Data analyses were performed using descriptive statistics and Wilcoxon signed-rank test

Health & Social Work VOLUME 49, NUMBER 2 MAY 2024

(i.e., a nonparametric test of the paired sample t test, since the sample size is under 100) in order to examine the changes in the outcomes. First, simple univariate descriptive statistics were conducted to describe the sample. Second, for unadjusted comparisons between BMI and levels of nutrition knowledge, at baseline and postintervention, we used Wilcoxon signed-rank test.

RESULTS

Each participant's BMI and nutrition knowledge were compared before and after the program. First, there were no statistically significant differences in BMI before and after participating in the program. Second, there were statistically significant differences in nutrition knowledge before and after participating in nutrition education sessions among participants. The posttest ($\mu = 58.87$, $SD = 10.87$) was statistically significantly higher than the pretest ($\mu = 31.60$, $SD = 20.65$), and the mean increase of 27.27 was found to be statistically significant ($p < .01$, $\alpha = .05$). This indicates an 86 percent increase in the mean nutrition knowledge among participants after participating in the program (see Table 2).

DISCUSSION

In this pilot program, 15 children with ASD/DD from first-generation Korean immigrant families significantly increased their nutritional knowledge after a brief seven-week health promotion program focused on healthy eating, increased physical activity levels, and reducing weight. The instructions and materials were presented to the children once a week over a two-hour period, where nutrition education took place during the first hour and physical activities in the second hour. BMI did not change during this brief health promotion program. However, the results show statistically significant increased nutritional knowledge after the program.

These results are similar to the findings of Hinckson et al. (2013), who performed a 10-week school-based intervention. Children with ASD/

DD in that study similarly made healthier food choices and showed improved endurance in a six-minute walk test they used in their study. Interestingly, improved food choices were still observable after a 24-week follow-up period. The present study did not examine whether the increased nutritional knowledge was retained. However, the community agency staff reported anecdotes from the participants' parents about the positive impact of nutritional knowledge on their children's food choices at home. Further studies are needed to explore the long-term effects of nutrition knowledge on healthy food choices and overall health among the participants.

Presumably, this successful outcome was due in part to the cultural adaptations that were made to align the nutritional information with hands-on experiences in making healthy Korean snacks and food choices. In the nutrition field, there is a growing awareness of the importance of addressing a lack of representation of diverse foods as examples of healthy eating and a gap in culturally sensitive nutrition guidance. As such, the recently updated *Dietary Guidelines for Americans 2020–2025* (particularly "Guideline 2: Customize and Enjoy Food and Beverage Choices to Reflect Personal Preferences, Cultural Traditions, and Budgetary Considerations") emphasized meeting dietary recommendations while keeping cultural preferences in mind (USDA & U.S. Department of Health and Human Services, 2020).

Some limitations of this analysis should be noted. First, this study used a quasiexperimental design, which is a one-group design with a pretest and posttest. It can be used to determine, on a general level, how the program affects a particular group and is suitable for conducting a pilot study. However, the differences between the pretest and posttest could be due to many threats to internal validity (e.g., maturation, testing effects, and differential selection of research participants) rather than to the program. Also, there are possible covariates such as family (e.g., family rules for eating), culture (e.g., child's place of

Table 2: Descriptive Statistics and Wilcoxon Signed-Rank *t*-Test Results for Nutrition Knowledge (*N* = 15)

| Outcome | Pretest | | Posttest | | 95% CI for Mean | z | df |
	M	*SD*	*M*	*SD*			
Nutrition knowledge	31.60	20.65	58.87	10.87	[−39.61, −14.93]	−2.99**	14

**p < .01.

birth, shame and stigma within their community), and school variables (e.g., accessible nutrition education in classrooms) that might have an impact on the outcome variables. Future studies should include covariates within a multilevel framework. Second, the sample was not randomly drawn from a population, so the difference between the pretest and posttest is not generalizable to the population from which the sample was drawn (Grinnell et al., 2016). Third, our small sample size limits our statistical power, and limited geographic location may reduce the generalizability of our findings. Fourth, the outcome variable was nutrition knowledge that can lead to an action (i.e., healthy food choices), so participants can act against their knowledge. However, this pilot study is a preventive health promotion program, and it is only possible to act with knowledge. Last, more information about Korean immigrant families' language/cultural indicators is needed. For example, there is no information on the child's place of birth that can affect their food preferences and choices. However, we recruited first-generation Korean immigrant families who speak Korean at home and eat Korean food daily, indicating cultural preferences in food choices and the need for culturally sensitive nutrition guidance. More detailed indicators are needed for future research.

Despite these limitations, the findings demonstrate the effectiveness of a culturally adapted health promotion program for underserved children with ASD/DD from first-generation Korean immigrant families. Studies focusing on the issues of overweight/obesity in children with ASD/DD are emerging. Past studies often focused on the relationship between age, sex, and overweight in children with ID (Bandini et al., 2005; De et al., 2008; Stewart et al., 2009). However, few studies focused on the interrelationship between other risk factors such as culture, parental factors (including socioeconomic and immigrant status), dietary intakes, and weight status among Asian children with ASD/DD (Choi et al., 2012). The present study aimed to deliver nutrition education incorporating a culturally sensitive approach to children with ASD/DD from first-generation Korean immigrant families. When more cultures are represented in nutrition education for children with ASD/DD, rather than using a standardized curriculum based on typical Western diet, we can connect with immigrant families more meaningfully. This sensitivity may lead to more effective changes in healthy food choices. Previous studies focusing on Latino and African American youth with disabilities and their families also emphasized that health promotion programs need to be culturally tailored to the community of interest (Suarez-Balcazar et al., 2013; Suarez-Balcazar et al., 2016). It is recommended that practitioners consider discussing potential adaptations with families, paraprofessionals, and agency staff who work extensively with the community (Suarez-Balcazar et al., 2016). In addition, as shown in Healy and Marchand's (2020) study, novel approaches to nutrition and exercise interventions are needed. Their use of a private Facebook group in a web-based intervention showed a timely approach in the social media age. Increased flexibility is necessary for studies of children with ASD/DD and their families. Furthermore, future studies will need to be undertaken to determine how these initial gains in nutritional knowledge can be extended over time.

Although participants' BMI did not change during this brief health promotion program, we observed a significant increase in physical activity involvement among them when we provided a structured physical activity program at a level comfortable for each individual. Also, we designed physical activity sessions where the intensity and duration of the exercise increased gradually over time to accommodate individuals' needs to improve cardiovascular endurance, strength, and flexibility. Many factors can work against efforts to increase physical activity levels in a family with a child with ASD/DD. In addition to parental time constraints, safety, and childcare considerations, many Korean immigrant families still feel the stigma and shame in simple activities, such as walking in the community with their child with a disability. Overweight/obesity prevention programs are not likely to be effective without understanding the prevalence and risk factors of overweight and obesity for children with ASD/DD, particularly among immigrant populations (J. H. Rimmer et al., 2010). Therefore, further examination is needed to explore children's risk factors, eating behavior patterns, and cultural risk factors that may influence the development of overweight and obesity (Choi et al., 2012).

CONCLUSION
The findings of this pilot study indicate the effectiveness of a culturally adapted health promotion program for children with ASD/DD in first-

generation Korean immigrant families. Asians are the fastest-growing population of new immigrants and comprise different ethnic subgroups, indicating the urgent need to develop, implement, and evaluate culturally adapted health promotion programs. The findings are encouraging, as they demonstrate that a brief culturally adapted health promotion program can make a difference in nutrition knowledge that can lead to healthy food choices and physical activity involvement. Future studies will need to be undertaken to determine how these initial gains in nutrition knowledge can be extended over time, as well as explore children's risk factors, eating behavior patterns, and other cultural variables that may influence the development of overweight/obesity and overall health. HSW

REFERENCES

Bandini, L. G., Anderson, S. E., Curtin, C., Cermak, S., Evans, E. W., Scampini, R., Maslin, M., & Must, A. (2010). Food selectivity in children with autism spectrum disorders and typically developing children. *Journal of Pediatrics*, *157*, 259–264. https://doi.org/10.1016/j.jpeds.2010.02.013

Bandini, L. G., Curtin, C., Fleming, R. K., Maslin, M. C., & Scampini, R. (2013). *Health U.: A nutrition curriculum for teenagers with intellectual and developmental disabilities.* CreateSpace Independent Publishing Platform.

Bandini, L. G., Curtin, C., Hamad, C., Tybor, D. J., & Must, A. (2005). Prevalence of overweight in children with developmental disorders in the continuous national health and nutrition examination survey (NHANES) 1999–2002. *Journal of Pediatrics*, *146*, 738–743. https://doi.org/10.1016/j.jpeds.2005.01.049

Bandini, L. G., Curtin, C., Phillips, S., Anderson, S. E., Maslin, M., & Must, A. (2017). Changes in food selectivity in children with autism spectrum disorder. *Journal of Autism and Developmental Disorders*, *47*, 439–446. https://doi.org/10.1007/s10803-016-2963-6

Centers for Disease Control and Prevention. (n.d.). *BMI percentile calculator for child and teen* [Database]. Retrieved June 12, 2023, from https://www.cdc.gov/healthyweight/bmi/calculator.html

Chang, S. (2017, September 26). *Back to basics: All about MyPlate food groups.* https://www.usda.gov/media/blog/2017/09/26/back-basics-all-about-myplate-food-groups

Choi, E., Park, H., Ha, Y., & Hwang, W. J. (2012). Prevalence of overweight and obesity in children with intellectual disabilities in Korea. *Journal of Applied Research in Intellectual Disabilities*, *25*, 476–483. https://doi.org/10.1111/j.1468-3148.2012.00694.x

Curtin, C., Anderson, S. E., Must, A., & Bandini, L. (2010). The prevalence of obesity in children with autism: A secondary data analysis using nationally representative data from the National Survey of Children's Health. *BMC Pediatrics*, *10*, Article 11.

De, S., Small, J., & Baur, L. A. (2008). Overweight and obesity among children with developmental disabilities. *Journal of Intellectual & Developmental Disability*, *33*, 43–47. https://doi.org/10.1080/13668250701875137

Egan, A. M., Dreyer, M. L., Odar, C. C., Beckwith, M., & Garrison, C. B. (2013). Obesity in young children with autism spectrum disorders: Prevalence and associated factors. *Childhood Obesity*, *9*, 125–131. https://doi.org/10.1089/chi.2012.0028

Golubović, S., Maksimović, J., Golubović, B., & Glumbić, N. (2012). Effects of exercise on physical fitness in children with intellectual disability. *Research in Developmental Disabilities*, *33*, 608–614. https://doi.org/10.1016/j.ridd.2011.11.003

Gregor, S., Bruni, N., Grkinic, P., Schwartz, L., McDonald, A., Thille, P., Gabison, S., Gibson, B. E., & Jachyra, P. (2018). Parents' perspectives of physical activity participation among Canadian adolescents with autism spectrum disorders. *Research in Autism Spectrum Disorders*, *48*, 53–62. https://doi.org/10.1016/j.rasd.2018.01.007

Grinnell, R. M, Jr., Williams, M., & Unrau, Y. A. (2016). *Research methods for social workers: An introduction* (11th ed.). Pair Bond Publications.

Ha, Y., Jacobson Vann, J. C., & Choi, E. (2010). Prevalence of overweight and mothers' perception of weight status of their children with intellectual disabilities in South Korea. *Journal of School Nursing*, *26*, 212–222.

Haveman, M., Heller, T., Lee, L., Maaskant, M., Shooshtari, S., & Strydom, A. (2010). Major health risks in aging persons with intellectual disabilities: An overview of recent studies. *Journal of Policy and Practice in Intellectual Disabilities*, *7*, 59–69.

Healy, S., & Marchand, G. (2020). The feasibility of Project CHASE: A Facebook-delivered, parent-mediated physical activity intervention for children with autism. *International Journal of Disability, Development and Education*, *67*, 225–242. https://doi.org/10.1080/1034912X.2019.1597968

Hillier, A., Murphy, D., & Ferrara, C. (2011). A pilot study: Short-term reduction in salivary cortisol following low level physical exercise and relaxation among adolescents and young adults on the autism spectrum. *Stress & Health*, *27*, 395–402.

Hinckson, E. A., & Curtis, A. (2013). Measuring physical activity in children and youth living with intellectual disabilities: A systematic review. *Research in Developmental Disabilities*, *34*, 72–86. https://doi.org/10.1016/j.ridd.2012.07.022

Hinckson, E. A., Dickinson, A., Water, T., Sands, M., & Penman, L. (2013). Physical activity, dietary habits and overall health in overweight and obese children and youth with intellectual disability or autism. *Research in Developmental Disabilities*, *34*, 1170–1178. https://doi.org/10.1016/j.ridd.2012.12.006

Huang, J., Du, C., Liu, J., & Tan, G. (2020). Meta-analysis on intervention effects of physical activities on children and adolescents with autism. *International Journal of Environmental Research and Public Health*, *17*, Article 1950.

Hubbard, K. L., Anderson, S. E., Curtin, C., Must, A., & Bandini, L. G. (2014). A comparison of food refusal related to characteristics of food in children with autism spectrum disorder and typically developing children. *Journal of the Academy of Nutrition and Dietetics*, *114*, 1981–1987. https://doi.org/10.1016/j.jand.2014.04.017

Lee, J., & Sheng, D. (2024). The Asian American assimilation paradox. *Journal of Ethnic and Migration Studies*, *50*, 68–94. https://doi.org/10.1080/1369183X.2023.2183965

Lopez, M. H., Passel, J., & Rohal, M. (2015, September 28). *Modern immigration wave brings 59 million to U.S., driving population growth and change through 2065.* Pew Research Center. https://www.pewresearch.org/his

panic/2015/09/28/modern-immigration-wave-brings-59-million-to-u-s-driving-population-growth-and-change-through-2065/

Lynch, L., McCarron, M., Eustace-Cook, J., Burke, É., & McCallion, P. (2022). Physical health effects of sedentary behaviour on adults with an intellectual disability: A scoping review. *Journal of Intellectual Disabilities.* Advance online publication. https://doi.org/10.1177/17446295221107281

Magaña, S., Dababnah, S., Xu, Y., Torres, M. G., Rieth, S. R., Corsello, C., Rangel, E., Brookman-Frazee, L., & Vanegas, S. B. (2021). Cultural adaptations of a parent training program for families of children with ASD/IDD: Parents taking action. *International Review of Research in Developmental Disabilities, 61,* 263–300.

Matheson, B. E., & Douglas, J. M. (2017). Overweight and obesity in children with autism spectrum disorder (ASD): A critical review investigating the etiology, development, and maintenance of this relationship. *Review Journal of Autism and Developmental Disorders, 4,* 142–156. https://doi.org/10.1007/s40489-017-0103-7

Memari, A. H., Mirfazeli, F. S., Kordi, R., Shayestehfar, M., Moshayedi, P., & Mansournia, M. A. (2017). Cognitive and social functioning are connected to physical activity behavior in children with autism spectrum disorder. *Research in Autism Spectrum Disorders, 33,* 21–28. https://doi.org/10.1016/j.rasd.2016.10.001

Menear, K. S., & Neumeier, W. H. (2015). Promoting physical activity for students with autism spectrum disorder: Barriers, benefits, and strategies for success. *Journal of Physical Education, Recreation & Dance, 86,* 43–48.

Rimmer, J. A., & Rowland, J. L. (2008). Physical activity for youth with disabilities: A critical need in an underserved population. *Developmental Neurorehabilitation, 11,* 141–148.

Rimmer, J. H., Yamaki, K., Lowry, B. D., Wang, E., & Vogel, L. C. (2010). Obesity and obesity-related secondary conditions in adolescents with intellectual/developmental disabilities. *Journal of Intellectual Disability Research, 54,* 787–794.

Schalock, R. L., Borthwick-Duffy, S. A., Bradley, V. J., Buntinx, W. H., Coulter, D. L., Craig, E. M., Gomez, S. C., Lachapelle, Y., Luckasson, R., & Reeve, A. (2009). *Intellectual disability: Definition, classification, and systems of supports* (11th ed.). American Association on Intellectual and Developmental Disabilities.

Son, E., Moring, N. S., Igdalsky, L., & Parish, S. L. (2018). Navigating the health-care system in community: Perspectives from Asian immigrant parents of children with special health-care needs. *Journal of Child Health Care, 22,* 251–268. https://doi.org/10.1177/1367493517753084

Srinivasan, S. M., Pescatello, L. S., & Bhat, A. N. (2014). Current perspectives on physical activity and exercise recommendations for children and adolescents with autism spectrum disorders. *Physical Therapy, 94,* 875–889. https://doi.org/10.2522/ptj.20130157

Sritharan, B., & Koola, M. M. (2019). Barriers faced by immigrant families of children with autism: A program to address the challenges. *Asian Journal of Psychiatry, 39,* 53–57.

Stewart, L., Van de Ven, L., Katsarou, V., Rentziou, E., Doran, M., Jackson, P., Reilly, J. J., & Wilson, D. (2009). High prevalence of obesity in ambulatory

children and adolescents with intellectual disability. *Journal of Intellectual Disability Research, 53,* 882–886.

Suarez, M. A., & Crinion, K. M. (2015). Food choices of children with autism spectrum disorders. *International Journal of School Health, 2,* 1–5.

Suarez-Balcazar, Y., Friesema, J., & Lukyanova, V. (2013). Culturally competent interventions to address obesity among African American and Latino children and youth. *Occupational Therapy in Health Care, 27,* 113–128. https://doi.org/10.3109/07380577.2013.785644

Suarez-Balcazar, Y., Hoisington, M., Orozco, A. A., Arias, D., Garcia, C., Smith, K., & Bonner, B. (2016). Benefits of a culturally tailored health promotion program for Latino youth with disabilities and their families. *American Journal of Occupational Therapy, 70,* Article 7005180080. https://doi.org/10.5014/ajot.2016.021949

U.S. Department of Agriculture & U.S. Department of Health and Human Services. (2020). *Dietary guidelines for Americans, 2020–2025* (9th ed.). https://www.dietaryguidelines.gov/

West, E. A., Travers, J. C., Kemper, T. D., Liberty, L. M., Cote, D. L., McCollow, M. M., & Stansberry Brusnahan, L. L. (2016). Racial and ethnic diversity of participants in research supporting evidence-based practices for learners with autism spectrum disorder. *Journal of Special Education, 50,* 151–163.

Yarimkaya, E., İlhan, E. L., & Karasu, N. (2017). Investigation of changes in communication skills of an individual with autism spectrum disorder participating in peer-mediated adapted physical activities. *Ankara University Faculty of Educational Sciences Journal of Special Education, 18,* 225–252. https://doi.org/10.21565/ozelegitimdergisi.319423

Zhao, M., & Chen, S. (2018). The effects of structured physical activity programs on social interaction and communication for children with autism. *BioMed Research International, 2018,* Article e1825046. https://doi.org/10.1155/2018/1825046

Zimmer, M. H., Hart, L. C., Manning-Courtney, P., Murray, D. S., Bing, N. M., & Summer, S. (2012). Food variety as a predictor of nutritional status among children with autism. *Journal of Autism and Developmental Disorders, 42,* 549–556.

Zuckerman, K. E., Hill, A. P., Guion, K., Voltolina, L., & Fombonne, E. (2014). Overweight and obesity: Prevalence and correlates in a large clinical sample of children with autism spectrum disorder. *Journal of Autism and Developmental Disorders, 44,* 1708–1719. https://doi.org/10.1007/s10803-014-2050-9

Esther Son, PhD, MSW, *is associate professor, Department of Social Work, School of Health Sciences, College of Staten Island, City University of New York, 2800 Victory Boulevard, Staten Island, NY 10314, USA; email: esther.son@csi.cuny.edu.* ***Sabretta Alford, LMSW, MPhil,*** *is a PhD candidate in social welfare, Graduate Center, City University of New York, New York, NY, USA.*

Original manuscript received February 15, 2023
Final revision received June 13, 2023
Editorial decision July 24, 2023
Accepted July 24, 2023
Advance Access Publication March 19, 2024

APPENDIX: HEALTH PROMOTION PROGRAM

The program consisted of a seven-week intervention. Each of the seven sessions covered two components: nutrition education and physical activity. The program also comprised one-hour health and nutrition education, including children with autism spectrum disorder and developmental disabilities learning to make and eat a healthy snack, and one hour of physical activities, including warm-up, stretching, strengthening, conditioning, and basketball drills/yoga, led by a sports/yoga instructor. Each week we discuss a different theme. See outline of themes for nutrition education and related activities as well as physical activities in the following sections.

1. Introduction to the Program and MyPlate Model

- Theme: general overview of the program and introduction to MyPlate model
- Nutrition activities: discussion of "what is a healthy lifestyle?"; understanding definitions of nutrition, energy, variety, vitamins, physical activity, and exercise using flashcards and five food groups of the MyPlate model, with printed photographs of individual foods including Korean food; and healthy snack eating (i.e., baked Korean sweet potatoes called *goguma*)
- Physical activities: warm-up (basic stretches and conditioning: light jog from a baseline to baseline) and basketball drills (dribbling)

2. Vegetables and Fruit

- Theme: vegetables and fruit
- Nutrition activities: coloring pages and worksheets with titles and themes such as "Vegetables keep you healthy!"; "What's your favorite fruit?"; and "I SPY fruits & veggies"; healthy snack making (i.e., fruit platter consisting of Korean pears, persimmons, apples, and grapes)
- Physical activities: warm-up (basic stretches and conditioning: light jog from baseline to baseline, side-step) and basketball drills (dribbling)

3. Dairy and Drinks

- Theme: learn about limiting sugar consumption in drinks
- Nutrition activities: discussion on the benefits of calcium and methods to increase daily calcium intake and the benefits of water and methods to increase daily water intake; understanding the dairy/drinks food group of the MyPlate model, using printed photographs of individual foods, including Korean foods; healthy snack making (i.e., making healthy air-popped popcorn using fresh popcorn kernels)
- Physical activities: warm-up (basic stretches and conditioning: light jog from baseline to baseline, side-step, and knee touches) and basketball drills (passing)

4. Proteins and Fats

- Theme: learn about strategies for limiting fat intake through consumption of healthy proteins
- Nutrition activities: understanding the proteins food group of the MyPlate model, using printed photographs of individual foods, including Korean foods; healthy snack making (i.e., a wrap sandwich filled with turkey, lettuce, and tomato)
- Physical activities: warm-up (basic stretches and conditioning: light jog from baseline to baseline, side-step, knee touches, and cone running) and basketball drills (passing)

5. Grains

- Theme: learn about whole wheat grains and benefits for our diet
- Nutrition activities: understanding the grains food group of the MyPlate model, using printed photographs of individual foods, including Korean foods; rainbow eating chart coloring; and healthy snack making (*yubucho-bap*, a dish made with seasoned fried tofu pockets and rice)
- Physical activities: yoga with a yoga instructor

6. Eating Healthy Portions

- Theme: learn about eating healthy portions
- Nutrition activities: learn and sing a "healthy eating song"; healthy snack making (snowman cheese stick)
- Physical activities: warm-up (basic stretches and conditioning: light jog from baseline to baseline, side-step, knee touches, and cone running) and basketball drills (shooting)

7. Review of MyPlate Model and Five Food Groups

- Theme: review of MyPlate model and five food groups

- Nutrition activities: learn and watch a video clip titled *You Are What You Eat*; healthy snack making (bananas, oats, and chocolate rolled up in a whole grain wrap)
- Physical activities: warm-up (basic stretches and conditioning: light jog from baseline to baseline, side-step, knee touches, and cone running) and basketball drills (shooting)

TREATING THE EATING DISORDER SELF

A COMPREHENSIVE MODEL FOR THE SOCIAL WORK THERAPIST

MARY ANNE COHEN

Mary Anne Cohen, LCSW, director of the New York Center for Eating Disorders, brings over 40 years of experience working with clients struggling with an eating disorder. In this engaging and compassionate book, Cohen teaches therapists how to fearlessly reach out to the heart and humanity of each client, illustrating how the therapist–client relationship—with its sharing of tears and laughter—makes treatment a deeply healing experience.

Integrating over 200 case examples, Cohen explores the two worlds of the binge eater, bulimic, and anorexic: the inner and the outer. In part 1, she delves into the inner world of frozen grief, depression, abuse, and early attachment. She presents attachment theory, how to conduct an eating disorder evaluation, how to blend psychotherapy and cognitive–behavioral strategies, the role of medications, and the ingredients needed for a healing therapeutic relationship. In part 2, she demonstrates how clinicians can develop multicultural, gender, and social media competency. Literacy in these three areas brings us a deeper understanding of the impact that this outer world has on the eating disorder patient and how to intervene to modify the harmful effects.

ISBN: 978-0-87101-550-1. 2020.
Item #5501. 252 pages.
1-800-227-3590
www.naswpress.org
CODE: APTEDS20

NASW PRESS

NASW
National Association of Social Workers

Examining Women's HIV Protective Behaviors in Nepal

Shambika Raut and Njeri Kagotho

Women's autonomy in decision making has important sexual and reproductive health implications. This study uses a nationwide analysis in Nepal to examine women's autonomy, attitude toward intimate partner violence (IPV) behaviors, and HIV-related knowledge in the execution of HIV protective behaviors such as having one sexual partner or getting an HIV test to prevent HIV transmission. Secondary data analysis was conducted using the nationally represented Nepal Demographic and Health Survey (2016–2021) dataset. The sample included 9,904 women ages 15 to 49 who self-identified as ever married. Factor analysis for women's autonomy, attitude toward IPV behaviors, and HIV-related knowledge were conducted based on social dominance theory. Structural equation modeling was conducted, and the results indicated that higher autonomy decreased the risk of HIV infection through having one sexual partner. Factors related to multiple sex partners included unemployment, religious affiliation, and age. Similarly, higher autonomy, HIV-related knowledge, having a formal job, and urban residence increased women's likelihood of taking an HIV test. Women's higher education, greater wealth, religious affiliation, and youth also correlate with HIV testing. Future HIV prevention interventions should include strategies that support women's social and economic empowerment and enhance women's ability to make informed choices about their health and risks.

KEY WORDS: *HIV and AIDS knowledge; HIV protective behaviors; intimate partner violence; Nepal Demographic Health Survey 2016; women's autonomy*

It is estimated that 0.12 percent of Nepal's population (approximately 30,000 people) currently live with HIV, with four out of five infections transmitted through sexual intercourse (UNAIDS, 2019). As with most Asian countries, Nepal continues to make modest progress in mitigating and addressing the epidemic (UNAIDS, 2020b). An estimated 79 percent of women and 77 percent of men living with HIV know their status, and among this group, 92 percent of women and 69 percent of men are in treatment (and of those, 89 percent of women and 86 percent of men have viral suppression; UNAIDS, 2020a). While HIV testing is provided free of cost through government and nongovernment HIV testing sites all over Nepal, there is reported underutilization of these services, with the lifetime prevalence of HIV testing being 18 percent among men and 7.4 percent among women (Sharma & Nam, 2019).

Globally, the number of women and girls living with HIV has surpassed the number of men (UNAIDS, 2022). Recent data indicate a decreasing male-to-female ratio of HIV infection in Nepal. In 2004, the estimated male-to-female ratio of infection was 2.4:1, with a decreased ratio of approximately 3:2 in 2018 (UNAIDS, 2019; UNAIDS & World Health Organization [WHO], 2004). Heterosexual intercourse is the most prevalent mode of HIV transmission in South Asian countries, including Nepal (Rodrigo & Rajapakse, 2009). The inability to negotiate safer sex practices has been identified as the major cause of increased HIV transmission among Nepali women. While Nepali women continue to bear an undue burden of disease, high prevalence has also been identified among marginalized groups such as female and male sex workers, intravenous drug users, men who have sex with men, the transgender community, and male labor migrants and their spouses.

Nepal presents a unique set of barriers and facilitators to HIV prevention and treatment. As one of the world's most disaster-prone countries, Nepal's heightened vulnerability to environmental crises, deeply entrenched patriarchal norms, and

https://doi.org/10.1093/hsw/hlae003   © 2024 National Association of Social Workers classification as a least-developed economy have constrained progress in HIV prevention. The resulting social and economic shifts, family disruption, labor migration, and increasing incidences of human trafficking have been documented barriers to HIV response. However, a vibrant civil society centering on women's experiences, and the move toward community-based healthcare task shifting, are promising facilitators of HIV prevention and treatment. WHO defines *task shifting* as the rational redistribution of tasks among health worker teams with tasks redistributed from highly qualified health workers to health workers with fewer qualifications who have been provided short-term training (WHO, 2008). The concept of task shifting has been used to support a range of health service demands in sub-Saharan Africa (Zachariah et al., 2009) including reducing the HIV burden. Community health workers and social workers as team members in task shifting play a pivotal role in improving help-seeking behaviors among people, reducing stigma and discrimination related to HIV and AIDS, and influencing adherence to HIV protective behaviors. Despite several benefits, task shifting has been identified as an expensive undertaking, and researchers are cautioned to propose it as a substitute for producing skilled health workers (WHO, 2008) for reducing the HIV burden.

Advancements in HIV prevention research are often attributed to clinical and biological science (Yaya et al., 2016). However, studying behavioral and sociodemographic factors presents social work researchers with opportunities to develop population-relevant interventions. Unfortunately, there has not been enough research assessing the factors associated with HIV protective behaviors in Nepal. The current study aims to bridge this gap by using the recent Nepal Demographic and Health Survey (NDHS) data to explore the relationships among women's autonomy, their attitude toward intimate partner violence (IPV), and HIV protective behaviors, and aims to address the following research question: What is the association between women's autonomy and their attitudes toward IPV and HIV protective behaviors, including HIV knowledge, HIV testing, and the number of sex partners?

LITERATURE REVIEW
HIV Risk and Violence against Women
Women's intersectional realities live within the context of harmful patriarchal systems, which means that they may experience these vulnerabilities differently and across multiple levels. Androcentricity and patriarchy, which are closely associated with women's increased exposure to violence and exploitation (Ahmed & Seid, 2020), have direct implications for sexual health. In most patriarchal societies, refusing sex within marriage is difficult as it can lead to the termination of the marriage (Wolff et al., 2000). As such, the matrimonial relationship can restrict women's ability to negotiate the conditions and timing of sex with their partners.

Autonomy and HIV
Adhikari (2016) defines *autonomy* as the ability to formulate choices, control resources, and partake in decision making. Women's autonomy is measured based on access and control over resources, involvement in economic decisions, self-esteem, and freedom of movement (Adhikari & Sawangdee, 2011; Basu, 1992; Kishor & Subaiya, 2008). Women with greater autonomy in decision making are more likely to negotiate safer sex (Atteraya et al., 2014). For instance, while condom utilization remains the major protection to reduce HIV and AIDS transmission (Ahmed & Seid, 2020), women's inability to ask their partners to use condoms puts them at higher risk of getting infected with sexually transmitted infections, including HIV (Feyisetan & Oyediran, 2020; Jesmin & Cready, 2014; Seidu et al., 2021).

Multiple Partners and HIV
Multiple and concurrent sexual partnerships and polygamous social norms in developing countries increase the risk of HIV infections (Adamczyk & Greif, 2011; Bloom & Griffiths, 2007; Sharma et al., 2017). The outcomes from several intervention studies suggest that reducing the number of sexual partners may not be more challenging than changing other sexual behaviors; however, research is needed to understand how meanings attached to multiple partners differ by gender (Kalichman & Grebler, 2010).

Knowledge about HIV
An individual's knowledge about HIV is a crucial determinant of their engagement in risky or protective behaviors. Lollis et al. (1996) found that individuals who are less knowledgeable about HIV do not perceive themselves as vulnerable and are more likely to engage in risky behaviors. Individuals with a higher level of education are more likely to

engage in HIV protective behavior (Bloom & Griffiths, 2007; Lindgren et al., 2005; Mengo et al., 2016; Snelling et al., 2007).

THEORETICAL FRAMEWORK

We use social dominance theory (Pratto & Walker, 2004; Rosenthal & Levy, 2010) as the guiding framework to analyze the relationship between autonomy and HIV protective behaviors. Rosenthal and Levy (2010) define *power* as the ability to act or behave according to one's wishes and the ability to influence or have control over the actions of others. As such, women's ability to choose with whom and how they have sex and to influence their partners to use protective measures such as condoms demonstrates their power. Rosenthal and Levy use the four bases of gendered power conceptualized by Pratto and Walker (2004)—force, resource control, social obligations, and consensual ideologies—to outline how gendered power dynamics heighten women's HIV risk.

Force

The first base of gendered power includes any form of violence against women that diminishes their power (Rosenthal & Levy, 2010). Women's experience of violence, whether in the form of childhood abuse or sexual abuse or being in an abusive relationship, increases their risk of contracting HIV (Ammann, 2002; Rosenthal & Levy, 2010; Shrestha & Copenhaver, 2016; Silverman et al., 2011).

Resource Control

The second base of gendered power emphasizes access to resources. The inequality in access and control over resources threatens women's sexual and reproductive health. Rural, poor, and less educated women are less likely than their urban, rich, and educated peers to exhibit assertiveness in their reproductive and sexual preferences (Amoyaw et al., 2015; Sano et al., 2018; Tenkorang, 2012). Women in Nepal have lower rates of house and land ownership, fewer employment opportunities, lower educational status, and weaker financial resources (Rawal & Agrawal, 2016).

Social Obligations

The third base of gendered power encompasses the responsibilities of women to others (partners, children, and family members). Women's roles of satisfying the needs and desires of others are socially

ubiquitous (Ford, 2018; Pratto & Walker, 2004; Rosenthal & Levy, 2010). The patriarchy in Nepali society amplifies the social expectations of subservience, therefore women's negotiation of safer sex practices is often considered defiance of the norm.

Consensual Ideologies

The final base of gendered power includes gender roles, norms, beliefs and expectations, and stereotypes (Rosenthal & Levy, 2010). Gender roles that are consistently asserted across cultures assign women to be passive acceptors and men as the controlling aggressors during sexual intercourse (Bowleg et al., 2004; Rosenthal & Levy, 2010; Scott et al., 2005). Thus, consensual ideologies such as gender norms and benevolent forms of sexism deter women's autonomy and increase the risk of being disproportionately affected by HIV.

METHOD

The present study performed secondary data analysis of nationally representative data from the NDHS 2016–2021 (New ERA, 2010). Data for this study were from the Woman's Questionnaire, which collected information on variables related to knowledge and behaviors regarding HIV and AIDS and domestic violence from 12,862 women ages 15 to 49. Using a subsample of only women who were ever married resulted in a final sample size of 9,904 ever-married women. (See Figure 1 for a conceptual framework of the study.)

Measures

Dependent Variables. Two variables were used to measure HIV protective behaviors The first outcome variable measured respondents' number of sexual partners, including spouses, in the previous 12 months and was dichotomized into "No, only with husband" and "More than husband." The second outcome variable measured if the respondent has ever been tested for HIV and was dichotomized into either no or yes.

Independent Variables. The independent variables were three latent variables: (1) women's autonomy, (2) permissive attitudes toward IPV, and (3) knowledge of HIV. Women's autonomy was measured by women's overall participation in multiple health and household decisions. Specifically, four questions were used to operationalize this latent variable: (1) Who usually decides on your

Figure 1: Conceptual Framework: Relationship between Women's Autonomy and HIV Protective Behaviors in Nepal

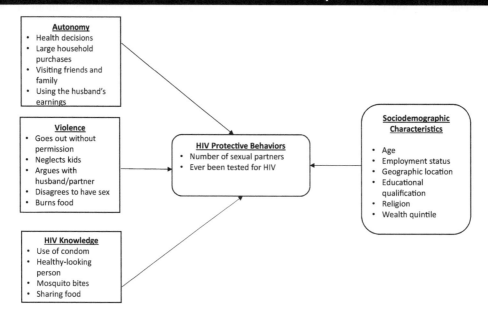

healthcare? (2) Who decides on making large household purchases? 3) Who decides your visits to family and relatives? and (4) Who decides what to do with your husband's earnings?

Attitude toward IPV was assessed with five variables based on women's responses to whether it is permissible for a husband to hit or beat his wife if she (1) goes out without telling her husband, (2) neglects the children, (3) argues with her husband, (4) refuses to have sex with her husband, or (5) burns the food.

Finally, HIV knowledge was measured with four variables based on whether the respondent (1) reported consistent use of the condom, (2) believed that a healthy-looking person can have HIV, (3) believed an individual can get HIV from a mosquito bite, or (4) believed an individual can get HIV by sharing a meal with an HIV-affected individual.

Sociodemographic Variables. Sociodemographic variables informed by past literature and theory included age, education, employment status, household wealth status, geographic province of residence (urban/city or rural), and religious identity.

Statistical Analysis

Data cleaning and univariate analyses of demographic variables were conducted using Stata 14 (StataCorp, 2015) and structural equation modeling

(SEM) using Mplus (Version 7; Muthén & Muthén, 2015). A polychoric correlation matrix and the weighted least square means and variance adjusted estimator were used to account for the categorical nature of observed variables (Flora & Curran, 2004). Mplus uses a pairwise present method of handling missing values when this estimator is used, which allowed all but two cases missing all scale data to be included in the analyses (Asparouhov & Muthén, 2010). Model fit was assessed using the root mean square error of approximation (RMSEA) with a point estimate and an upper 90 percent confidence interval (CI) value of less than 0.06 indicating a good fit. The comparative fit index (CFI) and Tucker–Lewis index (TLI) also were used, with values higher than .95 indicating a good fit (Bowen & Guo, 2011). The model χ^2 was also considered; however, because it is affected by large sample sizes, we did not expect a nonsignificant χ^2.

RESULTS

Of the entire sample of married women ($N = 9,904$), the average respondent was 32 years, with 41 percent reporting no formal education. The majority of the women were currently working (60 percent) and living (63 percent) in urban areas. Figures 2 and 3 provide a visual representation of the two general SEM models constructed in this study.

Model A: Sexual Partners

Model A examined the relationship between women's autonomy, HIV knowledge, and IPV and the number of sexual partners controlling for demographic factors. The model had good fit: ($N = 9,904$; $\chi^2(253) = 3,100.5$; $p = .000$; RMSEA = .034 (90% CI [0.033, 0.035]); CFI = 0.977, TLI = 0.974. Women's autonomous decision making was associated with sexual partners ($\beta = -0.126$, $p \leq .001$). Women with higher autonomy were less likely to report having more sexual partners. Similarly, women who worked were less likely to report multiple sex partners ($\beta = -0.023$, $p = .027$). Compared with Hindu adherents, Buddhists and Muslims were less likely to report multiple sex partners. Finally, older women were more likely to have more sexual partners ($\beta = 0.106$, $p \leq .001$).

Model B: HIV Testing

We tested the relationship between women's autonomy, HIV knowledge, and IPV and having been tested for HIV. The model had good fit: $N = 9,904$; $\chi^2(253) = 3,095.7$; $p = .000$; RMSEA = .034 (90% CI [0.033, 0.035]); CFI = .978; TLI = .975. Women's autonomous decision making ($\beta = 0.047$, $p \leq .001$) and HIV knowledge were associated with HIV testing ($\beta = 0.241$, $p \leq .001$). Women with higher autonomy and more HIV knowledge were more likely to have ever accessed an HIV test. Women who worked ($\beta = 0.021$, $p = .039$) and those living in urban areas ($\beta = 0.029$, $p = .009$) were more likely to have accessed an HIV test. Older women were less likely to have taken an HIV test ($\beta = -0.099$, $p \leq .001$). Women with postsecondary education were more likely than women with no schooling to have had an HIV test ($\beta = 0.094$, $p \leq .001$). As expected, compared with the poorest women, those in the highest wealth quintile were more likely to have had an HIV test ($\beta = 0.067$, $p \leq .001$). Finally, Buddhists ($\beta = -0.022$, $p = .045$) and Muslims ($\beta = -0.029$, $p = .041$) were less likely than Hindu adherents to have ever accessed HIV testing.

DISCUSSION

Consistent with earlier research findings from Nepal, India, Nigeria, Kenya, and Ethiopia (Adamczyk &

Figure 2: Relationship between Women's Autonomy, HIV Knowledge, and Intimate Partner Violence (IPV) and Number of Sexual Partners

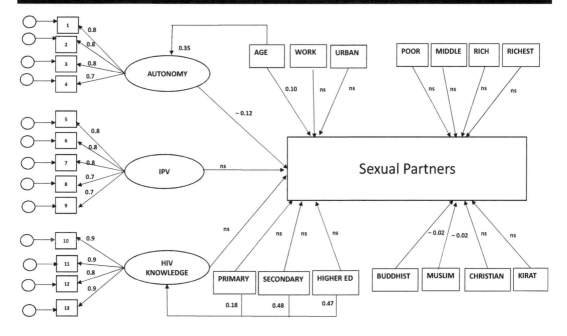

Notes: $N = 9,904$; $\chi^2(253) = 3,100.5$; $p = .000$; root mean square error of approximation = .034 (90% confidence interval [0.033, 0.035]); comparative fit index = .977; Tucker–Lewis index = .974.

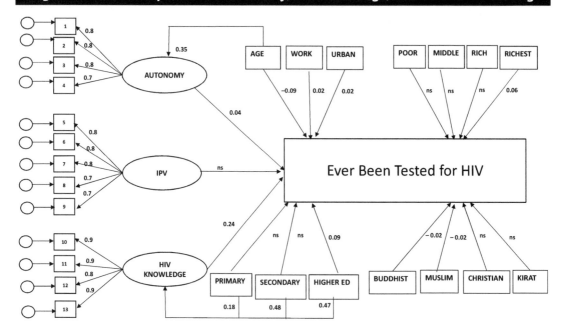

Notes: N = 9,904; $\chi^2(253)$ = 3,095.7; p = .000; root mean square error of approximation = .034 (90% confidence interval [0.033, 0.035]); comparative fit index = .978; Tucker–Lewis index = .975.

Greif, 2011; Ahmed & Seid, 2020; Bloom & Griffiths, 2007; Mengo et al., 2016), our study indicates that women's autonomy and knowledge of HIV and AIDS are positively associated with HIV protective behaviors. Taken in total, the present study concurs with earlier studies that suggest that increased gender equality and economic opportunities empower women to choose and maintain a safe sexual relationship. Nepali women with higher autonomy were less likely to have multiple sex partners; similarly, women with formal jobs were more likely to have only one sex partner. Contrary to our expectation, however, attitudes about IPV behaviors had no significant association with HIV protective behaviors. Earlier literature revealed that physical violence increases the likelihood of having multiple sex partners (Shrestha & Copenhaver, 2016; Silverman et al., 2011). However, our findings are consistent with studies that have found no association or a negative relationship between IPV and HIV protective behaviors (Teitelman et al., 2008; Tucker et al., 2004). This lack of association warrants further study but may be attributed to discrepancies in methodological and conceptual approaches to these measures.

The study found clear sociocultural determinants of HIV protective behavior including generational, regional, and religious differences. Older Nepali women were more likely to have multiple sex partners. Cultural practices of early marriages or multiple marriages in the past may have facilitated engaging with multiple sex partners (Mengo et al., 2016) for older respondents. Furthermore, older women reported less education than younger women in Nepal, and the existing literature does suggest that promoting girls' education and keeping them in school can delay marriage or cohabitation as well as increase their capacity to choose the nature of their sexual relationship (Lindgren et al., 2005; Mengo et al., 2016). This finding that higher education has a positive impact on health service utilization, as well as reproductive and sexual health-related outcomes, is further confirmed by data indicating that educated women in Nepal have a higher likelihood of getting HIV tests than their counterparts. Religious identity was also associated with HIV protective behaviors. When compared with their Buddhist and Muslim peers, Hindu adherents are more likely to report multiple sexual partners and more likely to have ever accessed HIV testing. These differences could be attributed to unique gendered norms, expectations, and stereotypes observed across each religious group.

Our findings indicate that future HIV prevention programs should develop a partnership with community organizations to increase HIV knowledge and awareness among women who live in rural areas and have lower education and wealth. As discussed, task shifting to community health workers and social workers can be a viable approach moving forward.

Social Work Implications

So far, the rate of decline in AIDS-related death is on track; however, the rate of decline in new HIV infections is off track for achieving Project 2030 (Assefa & Gilks, 2020). Moving forward, an all-inclusive strategy focusing on education for older women, poverty reduction, employment opportunities for women, and accessible healthcare in rural areas may pave the way for closing the gap in new HIV infections. While the social work profession is still nascent in Nepal, social workers in the country are equipped to address complex social issues in resource-constrained and crisis-prone environments. Social workers trained in innovative and participatory approaches have direct implications for the present study's results. For instance, these data show that living in rural areas decreases the odds of HIV testing for women, a finding that is not astonishing given that Nepal's centralized health services in urban areas limit access for rural Nepalis. Social workers would be key in future HIV prevention programs working to develop partnerships with community organizations to increase HIV knowledge and awareness among women who live in rural areas. Community-based programs in partnership with civil society in rural areas of Nepal provide multifaceted services to increase HIV- and AIDS-related knowledge and expand women's autonomy; these programs have the potential to play an important role in making progress toward improving women's sexual health. Grassroots initiatives such as Aama Samuha, or Mothers' Group, aim to empower and mobilize women through interventions that are responsive to the local milieu (Budhathoki, 2017). Task-shifting approaches can be used to mobilize women community health workers to spread knowledge about HIV prevention in rural areas.

While task shifting has the potential to address gaps in the public health workforce, the role of social workers in taking grassroots initiatives and task-shifting approaches to scale is critical. Integrating trained social workers with cross-cultural practice expertise can support lay workers in navigating underserved communities to help them prioritize tasks in resource-constrained environments.

Strengths and Limitations

This study has several strengths. To our knowledge, this study is the first of its kind to use SEM to examine the association of women's autonomy, IPV behaviors, and HIV knowledge with HIV protective behaviors among married women in Nepal. There also are several limitations to this study. First, due to the cross-sectional nature of the NDHS dataset, no causal relationship can be determined. Second, the data were collected in 2016 and may not capture current gender dynamics and HIV protective behaviors of women in Nepal. However, to our knowledge, no dataset of this magnitude is available for secondary analysis after 2016. Third, questions about attitudes toward IPV behaviors were self-reported, and this may have created social desirability bias and misspecification errors. Finally, our study captures the data only from married/cohabiting women and thus should be generalized with caution.

CONCLUSION

Like most Asian countries, Nepal continues to make modest progress in mitigating and addressing the HIV and AIDS epidemic. This study examines women's autonomy, attitudes toward IPV, and HIV-related knowledge in the execution of HIV protective behaviors. Results indicate that greater autonomy decreases the risk of HIV infection. Similarly, autonomy and appropriate knowledge about HIV increase the chances of taking an HIV test. Future HIV interventions should include strategies that support women's increased ability to make informed choices about their health and risks. HSW

REFERENCES

Adamczyk, A., & Greif, M. (2011). Education and risky sex in Africa: Unraveling the link between women's education and reproductive health behaviors in Kenya. *Social Science Research, 40,* 654–666.

Adhikari, R. (2016). Effect of women's autonomy on maternal health service utilization in Nepal: A cross-sectional study. *BMC Women's Health, 16,* Article 26.

Adhikari, R., & Sawangdee, Y. (2011). Influence of women's autonomy on infant mortality in Nepal. *Reproductive Health*, 8, Article 7.

Ahmed, M., & Seid, A. (2020). Does women's autonomy matter on attitude towards condom use in reducing risk for HIV infection among married women in Ethiopia? *HIV/AIDS (Auckland)*, 12, 489–496.

Ammann, A. (2002). The ongoing HIV epidemic [Student Editorial]. *BMJ*, 10, Article 325. https://doi.org/10.11 36/sbmj.0212442

Amoyaw, J. A., Kuuire, V. Z., Boateng, G. O., Asare-Bediako, Y., & Ung, M. (2015). Conundrum of sexual decision making in marital relationships: Safer-sex knowledge, behavior, and attitudes of married women in Zambia. *Journal of Sex Research*, 52, 868–877.

Asparouhov, T., & Muthén, B. (2010). Weighted least squares estimation with missing data. *Mplus Technical Appendix*. https://www.statmodel.com/download/GstrucMissingRevision.pdf

Assefa, Y., & Gilks, C. F. (2020). Ending the epidemic of HIV/AIDS by 2030: Will there be an endgame to HIV, or an endemic HIV requiring an integrated health systems response in many countries? *International Journal of Infectious Diseases*, 100, 273–277.

Atteraya, M. S., Kimm, H., & Song, I. H. (2014). Women's autonomy in negotiating safer sex to prevent HIV: Findings from the 2011 Nepal Demographic and Health Survey. *AIDS Education and Prevention*, 26, 1–12.

Basu, A. M. (1992). *Culture, the status of women, and demographic behaviour: Illustrated with the case of India*. Clarendon.

Bloom, S. S., & Griffiths, P. L. (2007). Female autonomy as a contributing factor to women's HIV-related knowledge and behaviour in three culturally contrasting states in India. *Journal of Biosocial Science*, 39, 557–573.

Bowen, N. K., & Guo, S. (2011). *Structural equation modeling*. Oxford University Press.

Bowleg, L., Lucas, K. J., & Tschann, J. M. (2004). "The ball was always in his court": An exploratory analysis of relationship scripts, sexual scripts, and condom use among African American women. *Psychology of Women Quarterly*, 28, 70–82.

Budhathoki, S. (2017). *Role of mother's group to women's empowerment*. Doctoral dissertation, Tribhuvan University Faculty of Humanities and Social Science, Central Department of Rural Development, Kirtipur, Kathmandu.

Feyisetan, B., & Oyediran, K. A. (2020). Can married or cohabiting women negotiate protective sex? Findings from demographic and health surveys of two West African countries. *Journal of Biosocial Science*, 52, 785–808.

Flora, D. B., & Curran, P. J. (2004). An empirical evaluation of alternative methods of estimation for confirmatory factor analysis with ordinal data. *Psychological Methods*, 9, 466–491.

Ford, L. E. (2018). *Women and politics: The pursuit of equality*. Routledge.

Jesmin, S. S., & Cready, C. M. (2014). Can a woman refuse sex if her husband has a sexually transmitted infection? Attitudes toward safer-sex negotiation among married women in Bangladesh. *Culture, Health & Sexuality*, 16, 666–682.

Kalichman, S. C., & Grebler, T. (2010). Reducing numbers of sex partners: Do we really need special interventions for sexual concurrency? *AIDS and Behavior*, 14, 987–990.

Kishor, S., & Subaiya, L. (2008). *Understanding women's empowerment: A comparative analysis of Demographic and Health Surveys (DHS) data* (DHS Comparative Reports 20). Macro International.

Lindgren, T., Rankin, S. H., & Rankin, W. W. (2005). Malawi women and HIV: Socio-cultural factors and barriers to prevention. *Women & Health*, 41, 69–86.

Lollis, C. M., Johnson, E. H., Antoni, M. H., & Hinkle, Y. (1996). Characteristics of African-Americans with multiple risk factors associated with HIV/AIDS. *Journal of Behavioral Medicine*, 19, 55–71.

Mengo, C., Small, E., Sharma, B. B., & Paula, U. (2016). Risky sexual behavior of multiple partner relations and women's autonomy in four countries. *Sexuality & Culture*, 20, 535–554.

Muthén, L. K., & Muthén, B. O. (2015). Examples: Mixture modeling with cross-sectional data. In *Mplus user's guide* (7th ed.; pp. 153–208). Author.

New ERA. (2010). *Integrated biological and behavioral surveillance survey among the wives of migrants in four districts of far-western Nepal: Round II*. https://www.aidsdatahub.org/sites/default/files/resource/ibbs-wives-migrants-nepal-far-western-districts-round-2-2010.pdf

Pratto, F., & Walker, A. (2004). The bases of gendered power. In A. H. Eagly, A. E. Beall, & R. J. Sternberg (Eds.), *The psychology of gender* (pp. 242–268). Guilford Press.

Rawal, D. S., & Agrawal, K. (Eds.). (2016). *Barriers to women's land and property access and ownership in Nepal*. International Organization for Migration.

Rodrigo, C., & Rajapakse, S. (2009). Current status of HIV/AIDS in South Asia. *Journal of Global Infectious Diseases*, 1, 93–101.

Rosenthal, L., & Levy, S. R. (2010). Understanding women's risk for HIV infection using social dominance theory and the four bases of gendered power. *Psychology of Women Quarterly*, 34, 21–35.

Sano, Y., Sedziafa, A. P., Vercillo, S., Antabe, R., & Luginaah, I. (2018). Women's household decision-making autonomy and safer sex negotiation in Nigeria: An analysis of the Nigeria demographic and health survey. *AIDS Care*, 30, 240–245.

Scott, K. D., Gilliam, A., & Braxton, K. (2005). Culturally competent HIV prevention strategies for women of color in the United States. *Health Care for Women International*, 26, 17–45.

Seidu, A. A., Aboagye, R. G., Okyere, J., Agbemavi, W., Akpeke, M., Budu, E., Saah, F. I., Tackie, V., & Ahinkorah, B. O. (2021). Women's autonomy in household decision-making and safer sex negotiation in sub-Saharan Africa: An analysis of data from 27 demographic and health surveys. *SSM Population Health*, 14, Article 100773.

Sharma, B., & Nam, E. W. (2019). Role of knowledge, sociodemographic, and behavioral factors on lifetime HIV testing among adult population in Nepal: Evidence from a cross-sectional national survey. *International Journal of Environmental Research and Public Health*, 16, Article 3311.

Sharma, B. B., Small, E., Mengo, C., & Ude, P. (2017). Women's autonomy and attitudes toward condom use: A multicountry analysis. *Social Work in Public Health*, 32, 238–253.

Shrestha, R., & Copenhaver, M. M. (2016). Association between intimate partner violence against women and HIV-risk behaviors: Findings from the Nepal demographic health survey. *Violence Against Women*, 22, 1621–1641.

Silverman, J. G., McCauley, H. L., Decker, M. R., Miller, E., Reed, E., & Raj, A. (2011). Coercive forms of sexual risk and associated violence perpetrated by male partners of female adolescents. *Perspectives on Sexual and Reproductive Health*, 43, 60–65.

Snelling, D., Omariba, D. W. R., Hong, S., Georgiades, K., Racine, Y., & Boyle, M. H. (2007). HIV/AIDS knowledge, women's education, epidemic severity and protective sexual behaviour in low-and middle-income countries. *Journal of Biosocial Science, 39*, 421–442.

StataCorp. (2015). Stata Statistical Software: Release 14.

Teitelman, A. M., Ratcliffe, S. J., Dichter, M. E., & Sullivan, C. M. (2008). Recent and past intimate partner abuse and HIV risk among young women. *Journal of Obstetric, Gynecologic & Neonatal Nursing, 37*, 219–227.

Tenkorang, E. Y. (2012). Negotiating safer sex among married women in Ghana. *Archives of Sexual Behavior, 41*, 1353–1362.

Tucker, J. S., Wenzel, S. L., Elliott, M. N., Marshall, G. N., & Williamson, S. (2004). Interpersonal violence, substance use, and HIV-related behavior and cognitions: A prospective study of impoverished women in Los Angeles County. *AIDS and Behavior, 8*, 463–474.

UNAIDS. (2019). *Country progress report—Nepal.* https://www.unaids.org/sites/default/files/country/documents/NPL_2019_countryreport.pdf

UNAIDS. (2020a). *Country progress report—Nepal.* https://www.unaids.org/sites/default/files/country/documents/NPL_2020_countryreport.pdf

UNAIDS. (2020b). *UNAIDS data 2020.* https://www.unaids.org/sites/default/files/media_asset/2020_aids-data-book_en.pdf

UNAIDS. (2022). *Fact sheet 2022.* https://www.unaids.org/sites/default/files/media_asset/UNAIDS_FactSheet_en.pdf

UNAIDS & World Health Organization. (2004). *Nepal: Epidemiological fact sheets on HIV/AIDS and sexually transmitted infections.* https://data.unaids.org/publications/fact-sheets01/nepal_en.pdf

Wolff, B., Blanc, A. K., & Gage, A. J. (2000). Who decides? Women's status and negotiation of sex in Uganda. *Culture, Health & Sexuality, 2*, 303–322.

World Health Organization. (2008). *Task shifting: Global recommendations and guidelines.* https://www.unaids.org/sites/default/files/media_asset/ttr_taskshifting_en_0.pdf

Yaya, S., Bishwajit, G., Danhoundo, G., Shah, V., & Ekholuenetale, M. (2016). Trends and determinants of HIV/AIDS knowledge among women in Bangladesh. *BMC Public Health, 16*, Article 812.

Zachariah, R., Ford, N., Philips, M., Lynch, S., Massaquoi, M., Janssens, V., & Harries, A. D. (2009). Task shifting in HIV/AIDS: Opportunities, challenges and proposed actions for sub-Saharan Africa. *Transactions of the Royal Society of Tropical Medicine and Hygiene, 103*, 549–558.

Shambika Raut, MA, *is a doctoral student, College of Social Work, The Ohio State University, 1947 College Road North, Columbus, OH 43210, USA; email: raut.21@osu.edu.* **Njeri Kagotho, PhD,** *is associate professor, College of Social Work, The Ohio State University, Columbus, OH, USA.*

Original manuscript received November 29, 2022
Final revision received February 10, 2023
Editorial decision July 24, 2023
Accepted July 26, 2023
Advance Access Publication April 3, 2024

ECOSOCIAL WORK
Environmental Practice and Advocacy

Rachel Forbes
Kelly Smith
Editors

S ince the earliest days of social work practice, social workers have dealt with environmental issues, advocating alongside diverse populations to address disproportionate environmental impacts on systemically marginalized populations including those living in poverty, populations of color, persons with disabilities, and women. In the face of the accelerating climate crisis, social workers must proactively engage with clients and communities and respond to the growing impacts of environmental injustices.

The American Academy of Social Work and Welfare's grand challenge to "create social responses to a changing environment" is a call to action for social workers to advocate for environmental justice. The Global Agenda, developed by the International Federation of Social Workers, the International Association of Schools of Social Work, and the International Council on Social Welfare, calls for multilevel responses to concerns such as forced migration, air pollution, ecoanxiety, and food and water insecurity.

Ecosocial Work: Environmental Practice and Advocacy answers that call with chapters that include theoretical frameworks and innovative tools. In this comprehensive text, the authors take a justice-centered approach as they draw on case examples to elevate multicultural and inter-generational perspectives spanning from local to global contexts. The book encourages readers to consider how simultaneously protecting the planet while meeting the historical aims of the profession advances the values and ethical mandates social workers abide by. Designed to foster critical thinking, the book offers hope and possibility for a just environmental future.

NASW PRESS

2023 · Item #5907 · 296 pages
1-800-227-3590 · www.naswpress.org

NASW
National Association of Social Workers

APEWE23

A Catalyst for Change: Intensive Care Unit Social Work Practice in the Post-COVID Era

Kerri Anderson, Sarah Andes Marquez, Kasey Pulley, Patricia Benninghove, Judy Kurzman,
Katina Harris, Joseph Roberts, Harley Jones, Tammie May, Ashena Thornton, Emily J. Dwyer, and
Bonita Hogue

V irginia Commonwealth University Health (VCUH) is a large academic and safety net hospital in Richmond, Virginia. Patients throughout the state and beyond our borders seek medical care from the various centers at VCUH. Social work is a core service for each acute care unit, including the intensive care units (ICUs). Social workers assigned to both adult and pediatric ICUs and members of department leadership have formed a team to address quality care, patient satisfaction, staff satisfaction, and cost containment. The team leads include members of the professions of social work and nursing, providing a dual perspective within the department.

INITIATIVE DESCRIBED

A three-pronged approach was used to guide the team's work. First, a literature review was completed to identify best practices. The work of Rose and Shelton (2006) on the role of social work in the ICUs was used to validate and expand social work roles and responsibilities. A tool initially developed in October 2002, "Psychosocial Pathway for Catastrophic Illnesses and Complex Care" (see Table 1) 2 was revised based on contemporary social work practice. The psychosocial pathway was designed with multiple phases, starting with four phases and adding an end-of-life phase. At VCUH, social workers share responsibility for planning and coordination of services with a nurse care coordinator. While the pathway focuses on the roles and responsibilities of the social worker, the diagram also reflects how the social worker collaborates with the nurse care coordinator. The team then focused on clinical documentation to reflect the standardized social work practice. VCUH recently transitioned to a new electronic medical record,

making this an opportune time to develop documentation templates specific for biopsychosocial assessments, progression to discharge notes, and family meeting notes.

The team was actively engaged throughout the process and worked efficiently with meetings lasting 30 to 60 minutes. Tasks were assigned for completion after each meeting to ensure that team members' time was utilized efficiently. Examples of tasks outside of meeting time included reviewing the literature, trialing the pathway, and piloting the new templates. The team quickly reached the performing phase of group development, rapidly completing major tasks. Leaders of the group observed swift development of mutual respect, camaraderie, and collaboration. Various members presented the team's work to the department at the conclusion of the project.

Sharing the Project and Documentation Templates

During the final staff meeting, several staff members shared feedback on how helpful the information documented on the new templates was in managing the care after the patient's transfer from the ICU setting. The non-ICU social workers were able to continue the work that was initiated in the ICU, with a good understanding of completed tasks, key players and decision makers, patient and family's values, and goals and preferences for further treatment or services.

Impact of the Pandemic

Visitation policies within hospital settings were immediately impacted by the pandemic. Visitors were restricted to specific visitation times, undergoing a health screening, and limited visitation spots per day.

Table 1: Psychosocial Pathway for Catastrophic Illnesses and Complex Care

Phase	Goals	Interventions	Outcomes
1 (days 1–2)	1. Verify identity of patient. 2. Verify insurance status of patient. 3. Mobilize family and determine family's understanding of current and projected health status. 4. Identify key decision maker. 5. Promote family cohesion by reducing conflict within the family and/or team. 6. Advance directive information gathered. 7. Barriers identified to accessing needed care posthospitalization; assess issues with access to care contributing to admission such as durable medical equipment, transportation, etc. 8. Obtain authorization for acute care services from insurer 9. Initiate referral for disability. 10. Initiate referral for Medicaid. 11. First communication with the family (usually a family conference) completed. The purpose of this initial communication is to orient the family to the team and begin discussion about the plan including the anticipated trajectory of options for the patient. 12. Enhance family engagement through participation in family meetings and decision making. 13. Assess prognosis in coordination with care providers.	1. ED registration clerk verifies patient identity and insurance information. 2. Team introduction to patient/family. 3. Physician/designee reviews clinical pathway with patient/family identifying usual hospital course, the customary or estimated length of stay, and anticipated disposition plan. 4. Physician discusses advance directives with patient/family. 5. Social worker engages with patient/family to provide psychosocial support and medical education appropriate to their diagnosis (stroke, trauma, transplant, palliative) and to initiate a discussion regarding postacute planning preferences to begin addressing anticipated needs. 6. Help family communicate patient's values and preferences and inquire about preferences for communication. 7. Address tangible needs such as transportation, caregiving, etc., and other concerns such as fear of hospitals, equipment in the ICU, getting bad news, feelings of guilt/anger/grief, visitation policy. 8. Social worker verifies benefits for posthospital care with insurer. 9. RN care coordinator provides clinical information to insurer for SI/IS criteria 10. Social worker and RN care coordinator refine discharge plan based on patient's progress, resources available, and LOS target. 11. Educate/counsel family on prognosis or trajectory of illness.	1. Patient identity verified. 2. Patient and family know who team members are for communication. 3. Patient/family/team understand the clinical pathway. 4. Acute care services are authorized by insurers. 5. Decision maker identified. 6. Development of a plan to address barriers to accessing needed patient care. 7. Financial screening process initiated via registration process.

(Continued)

Table 1: Psychosocial Pathway for Catastrophic Illnesses and Complex Care (Continued)

Phase	Goals	Interventions	Outcomes
2 (days 2–4)	1. Initiate patient care agreement for patients who have behavioral issues. 2. Continue to locate the family if needed. 3. Mobilize family for decision making. 4. Encourage shared responsibility of tasks among family members when feasible. 5. Enhance family engagement through participation in family meetings and decision making. 6. Affirm the family's coping strategies. 7. Initiate compassionate friend or guardianship process if needed. 8. Review options for ongoing treatment.	1. Team continues to provide support to patient/family by reviewing progress, treatment options, and treatment goals. 2. Social worker discusses options for posthospital care including inpatient rehab, short-term nursing home care for rehab, long-term nursing home care, palliative care hospice, psychiatry, ethics, pastoral care, or substance abuse consult. 3. Social worker assists patient/family in contacting Social Security Administration to schedule an appointment to apply for disability. 4. Social worker initiates the documentation required for nursing home placement, such as "Level II" PASRR, PCS, EMTALA/COBRA, or other forms needed to access care. 5. Help family communicate patient's values and preferences and inquire about preferences for communication. 6. Encourage family to visit the accepting facilities. 7. Issue a HINN when the first appropriate, available facility is confirmed. 8. Social worker faxes appropriate medical information to the disability claim analyst and Medicaid worker. 9. Social worker and RN care coordinator refine discharge plan based on patient's progress, resources available, and LOS target.	1. Team recommendation for disposition plan. 2. Assignment of Medicaid worker. 3. Appointment with Social Security for disability application. 4. Referrals made to appropriate facilities/service programs based on specific patient needs.
3 (days 4–7)	1. Provide patient/family information on providers of care who can meet the medical needs of the patient. 2. Verify insurance coverage for continuing care.	1. Physician/nurses reexamine the LOS target to determine appropriateness of target. 2. Social worker continues to address barriers. 3. Team reinforces recommended disposition plan.	1. Continuing care provider confirmed. 2. Insurance preauthorization obtained for the next provider of care.

(Continued)

Table 1: Psychosocial Pathway for Catastrophic Illnesses and Complex Care (Continued)

Phase	Goals	Interventions	Outcomes
	3. Schedule family meetings as needed to finalize discharge plan and to ensure agreement with long-term care planning: LTACH, SNF, IRF, assisted living, home health, hospice.	4. Social worker updates disability claim analyst on medical condition of patient. 5. Social worker and RN care coordinator refine discharge plan based on patient's progress, resources available, and LOS target.	
4 (days 7–10)	1. Disposition plan confirmed. 2. Provide handover communication to the next team caring for the patient.	1. Social worker arranges transportation for discharge. 2. All documents are completed without errors. 3. Facility-to-facility communication occurs to enhance continuity of care. 4. Assist in completing legal documents such as advance directives or durable DNRs, and provide copies.	1. Disposition on targeted date. 2. Variances noted. 3. Legal documents such as advance directives and durable DNRs are scanned in the patient's electronic medical record.
End-of-life phase	1. Assess for hospice eligibility. 2. Prepare patient/family for death in collaboration with chaplain and Decedent Affairs.	1. Complete legal documents such as last will & testament or minor guardianship requests. 2. Facilitate closure with family and friends. 3. Address spiritual concerns/needs. 4. Educate family on hospice benefit and structure. 5. Assess for complex bereavement needs and refer to counseling as appropriate. 6. Educate patient and/or family on end-of-life trajectory and expectations (i.e., imminent vs. days vs. weeks) to allow for planning for caregiving needs. 7. Help family prepare for postmortem expenses such as funeral planning, burial, or cremation costs. 8. Work with Decedent Affairs to provide next-of-kin contact information.	1. Family remains involved in end-of-life care plan. 2. Family is both emotionally and physically prepared for patient's end of life. 3. Identify appropriateness for levels of hospice care. 4. Faith traditions are honored including disposition of body.

Notes: ED = emergency department; ICU = intensive care unit; RN = registered nurse; SI/IS = severity of illness/intensity of service; LOS = length of stay; EMTALA/COBRA = Emergency Medical Treatment and Labor Act/Consolidated Omnibus Budget Reconciliation Act; HINN = hospital-issued notice of noncoverage; PASRR = preadmission screening and resident review; LTACH = long-term acute care hospital; SNF = skilled nursing facility; IRF = inpatient rehabilitation facility; DNR = do not resuscitate. This pathway starts when the patient is registered in the ED and continues until the patient is discharged, usually from the ICU or step-down unit. Days reflect optimal targets and can change based on the condition of the patient. The first choice of facility may not be available. Some patients will be discharged to facilities with plans to transfer to provider of choice when a bed becomes available.

These family presence limitations in the ICU setting changed how the ICU social worker facilitated communication between the family and the healthcare team. Communication between patients and their families was often through virtual means and often required creative solutions for family inclusion. Despite these challenges, VCUH social workers ensured families were engaged in decision making with their loved ones to determine goals and preferences for available services. Variables including access to health insurance benefits, location of the facilities, and star ratings factored into patient choice and were further impacted by the pandemic.

The pandemic exacerbated the impacts of grief for many families. Isolation and restrictions in physical presence or resources during the dying process complicated the role of the social workers. Social work support consisted of facilitating closure between patients and their families, assisting with legal documents, educating about trajectory of illness, providing information on available services and resources including hospice when appropriate, assessing for complex bereavement needs of family members, and helping family prepare for postmortem expenses.

A Focus on Palliative Care and Advance Care Planning

Once family members were not allowed into the healthcare setting, providers relied more heavily on social workers to identify the correct legal healthcare decision maker (LHDM). At VCUH, the ICU social workers went beyond identifying an LHDM to also identify and support the whole family system impacted by the patient's illness.

The importance of advance care planning was highlighted during this period of sudden illness and often rapid decompensation. Social workers worked diligently during admission to the ICU to ensure the patient's family system was known, documented, and reflected the patient's wishes for family engagement. Oftentimes social workers helped patients complete advance medical directives just prior to an urgent intubation to help the patient find comfort in knowing their preferences for healthcare treatment were known and would be honored by their family and medical team (Wallace et al., 2020). Medical decision making on behalf of a loved one has been shown to be highly traumatizing, particularly when the patient's wishes are unknown or death was not anticipated (Coelho et al., 2018). Facilitating discussions with a patient and their family are effective ways to decrease the risks of poor outcomes if an ICU admission results in the death of a patient (Wallace et al., 2020). Proactively completing advance medical directives is a way in which social workers help to honor a patient's healthcare preferences, promote healthy coping within family systems, and minimize costs of ICU care (Gwyther et al., 2005). Furthermore, facilitating difficult conversations to compassionately elicit healthcare preferences, spiritual practices, and familial understandings of illness are key to patient-centered decision making (Cain et al., 2018).

Palliative care is rapidly becoming more entwined in high-quality ICU care practices (Cain et al., 2018, Saga et al., 2018). The role of the palliative care team is known for providing end-of-life care, reducing a patient's symptom burden, and the associated spiritual distress in the process. Many of the goals of palliative care are similar to those of the social workers, such as supporting the family system, connecting to resources to achieve goals, and providing space to process and reflect on the emotional impact of the serious illness (Wallace et al., 2020). Social workers remain attentive to ensure all family members are included in meetings to help facilitate strong familial communication and coping beyond the hospitalization. During the pandemic, simply the inclusion of extended family members required creative solutions coordinated by social workers such as initiating hospitalwide policies and increasing access to resources for family communication. Social workers also advocated for necessary spiritual and religious practices at end of life, such as continuous family presence, visitation from religious leaders, or other cultural rituals (Cain et al., 2018).

NEXT STEPS

The team continues to meet regularly to focus on best practices, education, and peer support. Currently, they are developing protocols for advance care planning representing a culturally sensitive family-centered approach. A commitment to regular clinical training for this team is met with excitement and intent to continue to improve the quality of social work practice delivered in our organization. HSW

REFERENCES

Cain, C. L., Surbone, A., Elk, R., & Kagawa-Singer, M. (2018). Culture and palliative care: Preferences, communication, meaning, and mutual decision making. *Journal of Pain and Symptom Management, 55,* 1408–1419. https://doi.org/10.1016/j.jpainsymman.2018.01.007

Coelho, A., de Brito, M., & Barbosa, A. (2018). Caregiver anticipatory grief: Phenomenology, assessment and clinical interventions. *Current Opinion in Supportive & Palliative Care, 12,* 52–57. https://doi.org/10.1097/SPC.0000000000000321

Gwyther, L. P., Altilio, T., Blacker, S., Christ, G., Csikai, E. L., Hooyman, N., Kramer, B., Linton, J. M., Raymer, M., & Howe, J. (2005). Social work competencies in palliative and end-of-life care. *Journal of Social Work in End-of-Life & Palliative Care, 1,* 87–120. https://doi.org/10.1300/J457v01n01_06

Rose, S. L., & Shelton, W. (2006). The role of social work in the ICU: Reducing family distress and facilitating end-of-life decision-making. *Journal of Social Work in End-of-Life & Palliative Care, 2,* 3–23. https://doi.org/10.1300/J457v02n02_02

Saga, Y., Enokido, M., Iwata, Y., & Ogawa, A. (2018). Transitions in palliative care: Conceptual diversification and the integration of palliative care into standard oncology care. *Chinese Clinical Oncology, 7,* 32–32. https://doi.org/10.21037/cco.2018.06.02

Wallace, C. L., Wladkowski, S. P., Gibson, A., & White, P. (2020). Grief during the COVID-19 pandemic: Considerations for Palliative Care Providers. *Journal of Pain and Symptom Management, 60,* e70–e76. https://doi.org/10.1016/j.jpainsymman.2020.04.012

Kerri Anderson, LCSW, is clinical social worker, palliative care, Virginia Commonwealth University (VCU) Health, 1250 East Marshall Street, Richmond, VA 23298, USA; email: kerri.anderson@vcuhealth.org. **Sarah Andes Marquez, LCSW,** *is clinical social worker III;* **Kasey Pulley, LCSW,** *is social work clinician;* **Patricia Benninghove, MSW,** *is care coordination team lead, inpatient pediatrics;* **Judy Kurzman, MSW,** *and* **Katina Harris, MSW,** *are clinical social workers;* **Joseph Roberts, MSW,** *is clinical social worker, pediatric intensive care unit;* **Harley Jones, MSW,** *is clinical social worker II;* **Tammie May, RN, ACNS-BC, CCN,** *and* **Ashena Thornton, BSN, RN,** *are care coordination team leads;* **Emily J. Dwyer, BSW, RN, ACM,** *is registered nurse care coordinator and team lead; and* **Bonita Hogue, LCSW, C-SWHC,** *is social work manager, College of Health Professions, VCU Health, Richmond, VA, USA.*

Original manuscript received May 8, 2023
Editorial decision June 21, 2023
Accepted July 5, 2023
Advance Access Publication March 14, 2024

Leading
and
Managing
Nonprofit
Organizations

Edited by
RICHARD L. EDWARDS and
PAUL A. KURZMAN

Leading and managing a nonprofit is a complex, demanding, and often overwhelming task. Identifying concise resources that will help you build your leadership and management skills can be equally challenging, whether you are already in the boardroom or are aspiring to be.

Richard Edwards and Paul Kurzman have assembled over a dozen university faculty and field experts, providing best practices and thought leadership for turbulent times.

ISBN: 978-0-87101-568-6 • 2021
Item #5686 • 452 pages
1-800-227-3590 • www.naswpress.org

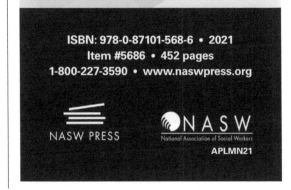

NASW PRESS

NASW
National Association of Social Workers

APLMN21

BOOK REVIEW

The Social Determinants of Health and Health Disparities. Paula Braveman. Oxford University Press, 2023, 320 pages. ISBN 9780190624118. $61.00 hardcover.

Even if social workers were to read only the introduction to this book, they would still come away with enough material—definitions, key points, questions for discussion, references—to challenge all their inherent biases and preconceptions regarding the impact of social factors on health and health disparities. However, it is in reading the entire text that social workers can begin to consider the potential significance of their roles in interrupting downstream health damage by working to create upstream health-promoting pathways.

Braveman, who has studied and published extensively on health equity and the social determinants of health, has written an academic text that can be adapted for multiple levels of social work education as well as multiple social work applications in the field. The text covers a wide range of health-related topics within a particular subject area, providing in-depth information in a clear and understandable manner. It offers foundational health disparity knowledge suitable for entry-level learners while also creating opportunities for delving into advanced concepts of social determinants for higher-level students or professionals. The format is flexible, allowing instructors or readers to adapt and select specific sections or chapters based on the level of expertise or specific application. It incorporates diverse pedagogical tools such as discussion questions, practical examples, and real-world applications. These elements help engage readers across various levels of health-related expertise and encourage critical thinking and application of knowledge.

Each chapter-ending discussion in this book opens avenues of inquiry for social work practice or research that prioritize health-promoting pathways, both informing and challenging social workers to define their practice beyond the traditional human services focus on "fixing" and the end result, providing services to ameliorate the marginalizing downstream impact of health-damaging pathways. Social workers, through ethical commitment to social justice, advocacy skills, and direct engagement with affected populations, are uniquely positioned to extend their roles beyond direct practice into influencing structural and systemic change, making their involvement indispensable in creating more equitable and just societies. Braveman seems to emphasize this point by reserving the insertion of a single chapter conclusion for the chapter on racism, calling the social work readers' attention to the irrefutable importance of addressing the universal impact of structural and systemic racism on all aspects of health and health disparity. Braveman's conclusions challenge social workers to address the fundamental upstream stressors of structural and systemic racism by adopting multifaceted approaches that involve individuals, communities, organizations, and policymakers in appreciating "the social experience of living in bodies perceived to be of different races" (p. 117). Social work researchers will appreciate the way Braveman acknowledges the dearth of conclusive or evidence-based knowledge of the most effective and efficient interventions to reduce upstream health disparities. Each chapter reminds the reader that broader and deeper discussion and research are needed to support and expand policies and programs already identified and promising to prioritize health-promoting pathways.

Social work educators will appreciate the way Braveman creates space for critical discussions about the complex and interrelated pathways of political and social influence in the context of health-related factors including behavior, early childhood experiences, education, employment, environmental hazards, housing, income, racism, stress, and wealth. The book gives examples and explores how these health-impacting pathways are made complex by resource allocation and funding priorities, policy and political priorities, and data and measurement challenges. Limited resources and funding constraints often lead human services agencies to prioritize interventions that directly address immediate health concerns or crises. This might mean allocating resources toward healthcare services that address illnesses rather than investing in broader social programs that promote health through education, employment, or community development. Policy decisions and political priorities can heavily influence the focus of human services. Short-term political cycles may favor visible and immediate results, making it more appealing to address immediate health concerns rather than

https://doi.org/10.1093/hsw/hlae005

investing in longer-term strategies that focus on prevention and health promotion. Measuring the impact and effectiveness of interventions on health-promoting pathways can be challenging compared with assessing the direct outcomes of treatments for health–damaging pathways. This difficulty in quantifying the impact of preventive measures might deter some agencies from investing in such initiatives.

Social workers are uniquely positioned to understand and address racial and social disparities that impact health; however, many find themselves uncertain or weak in determining their ability to impact upstream social factors that could eventually drive greater equity in downstream policy and subsequently empower marginalized individuals, communities, and societies. Each chapter ends with a pointed discussion of actions, initiatives, policies, programs, or strategies that may be instrumental in addressing upstream causes of socially stressful conditions, making neighborhoods healthier; mitigating, reducing, and eliminating structural and systemic racism; reducing economic, educational, and housing disparities; and removing obstacles to healthy behaviors. In creating a space for these critical and difficult discussions, Braveman has provided a well-referenced mechanism for responding to, and going beyond, what Burghardt (2021) refers to as the diminished state of social work education, which he believes has become unable to respond to social determinants of health due to focusing on cultural competency rather than combating structural and systemic racism. Braveman moves the reader beyond educating and encouraging cultural competence by striking a balance between depth of content and breadth of coverage, providing sufficient depth in key health-related areas while offering a broad overview that urges interdisciplinary social work action that will "improve the conditions in people's homes, schools, workplaces, and communities that powerfully shape people's opportunities to make healthy choices… [and] act to reduce the obstacles, particularly for those who face the greatest obstacles" (pp. 282–283). **HSW**

REFERENCES

Burghardt, S. (2021). *The end of social work: A defense of the social worker in times of transformation.* Cognella.

Sandra M. Sheppard, PhD, LMSW, CASAC-M
Evaluation & Analytics, CCNY, Inc. Buffalo, NY,
USA

Advance Access Publication March 13, 2024

MORAL DISTRESS AND INJURY IN HUMAN SERVICES

Cases, Causes, and Strategies for Prevention

FREDERIC G. REAMER

In this one-of-a-kind book, Frederic G. Reamer, the social work profession's foremost ethics expert, provides guidance to social workers and related professionals who grapple with these unwanted and unnerving situations and their aftermath, and inspires social workers to advocate for much-needed organizational and policy changes to prevent harm. Drawing on decades of first-hand experience, Dr. Reamer discusses moral distress, injury, and demoralization; the symptoms that can manifest; prevention, self-care, and resilience; legal and ethical obligations, including what it means to be a whistleblower; and how to develop moral courage.

Through extensive and relatable case studies, Dr. Reamer illustrates the myriad ethical dilemmas that most social workers will face in their careers and provides practical exercises and actionable solutions. This informative, enlightening, and inspiring book offers those who are struggling the guidance and fortitude to make the right decisions, and to strengthen themselves and their profession.

ISBN: 978-0-87101-560-0 • 2021
Item #5600 • 196 pages • 1-800-227-3590
www.naswpress.org

NASW PRESS

National Association of Social Workers

CODE# APMDI20

REVISED 3RD EDITION

ETHICAL STANDARDS IN SOCIAL WORK

A Review of the NASW *Code of Ethics*

FREDERIC G. REAMER

Ethical Standards in Social Work is a practical guide designed to help social workers protect clients, make sound ethical decisions, and minimize the risk of professional malpractice and disciplinary action. The revised third edition reflects the 2021 updates of the *Code of Ethics of the National Association of Social Workers*, which provides social workers with a comprehensive summary and analysis of ethical standards in the profession and an explicit statement of the profession's principal mission and core values. *Ethical Standards in Social Work* now includes extensive discussion of new and updated ethics standards, especially pertaining to cultural competence and social workers' self-care.

NASW PRESS

ISBN: 978-0-87101-594-5 (pbk).
2023. Item #5945. 336 pages.
1-800-227-3590 www.naswpress.org

National Association of Social Workers

APESS23

SOUTH ASIANS IN THE UNITED STATES

A Guide for Social Workers and Other Helping Professionals

Edited by Shreya Bhandari

Currently, about 5.4 million South Asians live in the United States, with family origins in India, Pakistan, Bangladesh, Nepal, Sri Lanka, the Maldives, and Bhutan. An intricate understanding of their immigration history, struggles with the immigration systems, and strong reliance on familial values is extremely important to serve the South Asian population in a culturally responsive manner.

South Asians in the United States debunks the myth of the "model minority," a term often used due to the rapid financial and cultural success of some of the South Asian subgroups. Instead, the authors have compiled comprehensive evidence-based literature on the prevalence, nature, and types of social issues that South Asians in the United States face, as well as how best to intervene. Using an intersectionality framework, the authors bring together previously fragmented research on this population and explain through case studies the myriad topics, including domestic violence, mental health, parenting, gender and sexual orientation, workplace barriers, and aging. Connections are made between intersectionality and postcolonialism, and the impact that various identities have on the health and well-being of this growing population.

This book is an urgent call for social workers and other helping professionals to combat sources of oppression that have disproportionately affected the South Asian population in the United States—racism, sexism, casteism, homophobia, and xenophobia. When we directly address these challenges, we offer understanding, sensitivity, and hope.

ISBN: 978-0-87101-582-2.
Item #5822. 220 pages.

National Association of Social Workers

1-800-227-3590
www.naswpress.org

NASW PRESS

APSAUS22

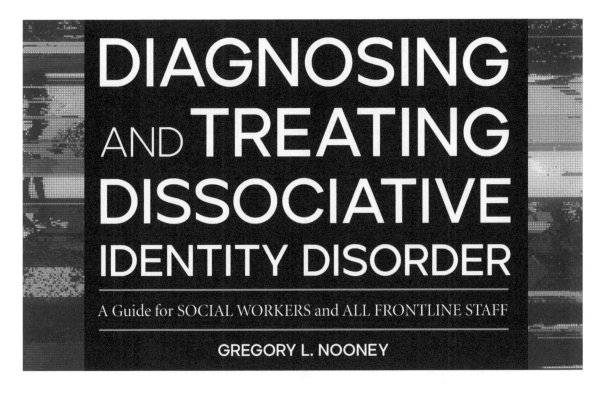

DIAGNOSING AND TREATING DISSOCIATIVE IDENTITY DISORDER

A Guide for SOCIAL WORKERS and ALL FRONTLINE STAFF

GREGORY L. NOONEY

Dissociative identity disorder (DID), previously known as multiple personality disorder, is a misunderstood and often underdiagnosed condition. Whether you are a new social worker or an experienced frontline staffer who is new to DID, *Diagnosing and Treating Dissociative Identity Disorder* is the resource that can help.

Using case studies, diagnostic tools, and clinician self-care, Gregory L. Nooney demonstrates how to confirm a DID diagnosis and establish a therapeutic relationship; assist the client in developing internal communication, cooperation, and co-consciousness; mitigate the risk of breaking dissociative barriers too quickly; manage the risk of rapid switching and decompensation, including suicidal risk; and lead the client from emotional rigidity and chaos to integration. Fortunately, because of the brain's plasticity and the effectiveness of trauma-specific treatments, healing is possible even for individuals who have experienced severe childhood trauma and attachment wounds. Though the challenges of diagnosing and treating DID are vast, the rewards of helping this misunderstood and underserved population are enormous.

NASW PRESS

ISBN: 978-0-87101-572-3. 2022. ITEM #5723. 202 PAGES.
1-800-227-3590 · WWW.NASWPRESS.ORG

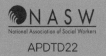

NASW
National Association of Social Workers

APDTD22

HEALTH &
SOCIAL WORK

H*ealth & Social Work,* established in 1976, is a professional journal committed to improving social work practice and expanding knowledge in health care. It is written for workers in all areas of the physiological, psychological, social, cultural, and environmental health sciences. Health is defined broadly to include both physical and mental health. The editorial board welcomes manuscripts on all aspects of health that are of professional concern to social workers. The journal carries articles on practice, social policy and planning, legislative issues, innovations in health care, and research.

The editorial board of *Health & Social Work* strives to include articles that appeal to its broad constituency, addressing both practice and policy issues. Related articles are often grouped in an issue. A call for papers on special themes may be issued on topics of major importance to the field, such as substance abuse or mental health.

Reviewers look for submissions to

- be important to social work and relevant to health
- contain a clear statement of purpose and a consistent focus
- expand current knowledge
- build on the work of others
- contain a current and appropriate literature review
- include relevant medical information, such as etiology, prognosis, and hereditary factors, if disease specific
- present complete methodology for a research article
- be well organized, with a logical, orderly presentation
- support conclusions with data or a logical argument
- contain a clear explication of the implications for social work.

ARTICLES

Manuscripts for full-length articles **may not exceed 20 pages,** including all components. The entire review process is anonymous. At least three reviewers critique each manuscript, after which the editor-in-chief makes a decision, taking those reviews into consideration.

COLUMNS

Practice Forum offers authors the opportunity to describe practice innovations and action research. It is designed to publish material that is important to and written by practitioners. Submissions should describe new and effective programs, techniques, or policies. The editor of the Practice Forum may assist authors in developing articles for the column. **Practice Forum submissions may be no longer than eight pages.**

National Health Line reports current legislative and political issues that have implications for social work practice in health settings. It provides a link between social work practice and health care policy. Written by the column editor, National Health Line presents contemporary issues that could have the greatest impact on social work clients. Suggestions for topics to be covered are invited.

Viewpoint features readers' comments and opinions on current issues in the profession. It offers writers an opportunity to express their opinion on issues that may have an impact on social work or social work clients in health or mental health settings. **Viewpoint submissions may be no longer than seven pages.**

Letters to the Editor enhance professional dialogue by providing readers the opportunity to comment on issues covered in the journal or other points of interest to social workers in health or mental health settings. Although we acknowledge and read all letters, not all can be published. Letters selected by the editor-in-chief may be shortened to fit the available space. **Letters to the Editor submissions may be no longer than two pages.**

To prepare your manuscript in the proper format for submission view *Writing for the NASW Press: Information for Authors* at http://www.naswpress.org/authors/guidelines/00-contents.html. Please submit manuscripts as Word documents through the online submission portal at http://hsw.msubmit.net (initial, one-time registration is required).